MRS

"Tell Us a Story"

108 Stories
for Primary School
Worship Assemblies,
with Prayers, suggested Hymns,
and Teachers' Notes,
for Autumn, Spring,
and Summer terms

Rev. Dr. George E. Stewart,
B.A., M.A.

Topical Resources

First Published September 1993
Reprinted June 1994
Reprinted June 1995
Reprinted May 1997

Published by:
Topical Resources,   P.O. Box 329,
Jumps Farm,   Broughton,
Durton Lane,   Preston,
Broughton,   PR3 5LT
Preston,
PR3 5LH.
Tel: 01772 863158

ISBN 1-872977-08-1

Typeset and Printed by T. Snape & Co. Ltd., Boltons Court, Preston, Lancashire.
Tel: 01772 254553

Preface

"Tell Us a Story," has been written for the Worship Assembly of the Primary School. Many of the stories are in print for the first time. The stories, prayers, and hymns are intended to be an aid to Worship for busy Primary Teachers.

The simple style and language of the stories has been chosen deliberately. The stories are meant to be told, rather than read. The style of story telling, has been adapted to suit the wide age range of Primary School pupils. The stories in this volume have been tested out, in the actual Primary School Worship Assembly situation. Qualified Teachers have constructively criticised them, and the style and language has been amended, where it was thought to be necessary.

The stories cover the three terms of a school year. Each week has a single theme, dealt with by two stories applicable to the children's life experience, and one story from the Bible. A short prayer is added after each story, based on the theme for the week. A hymn is suggested, taken from one of three popular Hymn Books used by Primary schools. A "Teachers' Note" has been added at the end of each story, which usually makes three valid points. The story as it unfolds, usually contains a moral, or a social problem, which is of interest to the children. They are meant be involved in the moral decisions, as the Teacher tells the story.

I have been influenced in my writing by the answers I received from a Questionnaire, which I sent out to thirty Primary schools. The Headteachers' reply listed the difficulties of the Worship Assembly, as: (1) The Pupil's limited attention span. (2) The Pupils live in a television age, and consequently, pictures come easier to children than words. (3) Worship is not always pitched at the child's age level. (4) Religion is not relevant to the parental background. (5) Pupils, generally, no longer attend Sunday School.

Although the book is based on the progression of the school year, the stories may be used individually to suit events in the school, or in the pupils' life experience. eg. An accident, a local celebration, a birthday, Christian Aid Week, a farewell, holidays, or the recognised special days. The choice is left to the professionalism, integrity, and sensitivity of the Teacher.

The stories have been written under the provisions of the 1988 Education Reform Act, where a distinction has been drawn between the Worship Assembly, and Religious Education. This book has been written with, "a broadly Christian Approach". It treats the stories objectively, without denominational bias. It leaves the matter of interpretation to the Teacher, and to the imagination of the children.

There are many stories here which could readily be used by Sunday school Teachers, or in Church Family Services.

Contents

Autumn Term

Spring Term

Summer Term

Hymn Book Abbreviations.

The suggested Hymns for these Worship Assemblies are to be found in one of three popular Hymn Books used by schools.

(C&P.1.) Come and Praise. Book 1.   B.B.C. Publications

(C&P.2.) Come and Praise. Book 2.   B.B.C. Publications

(JP.)   Junior Praise.   (Combined Words Edition)
                                      Marshall Pickering

Autumn Term

(a) Coming back to School and to Your Friends *Week 1 Friends*

It was the new term, and all the children were going back to school, after the Summer holidays. Most children walked to school, because the school was near their homes; Some children came in their parents' cars. Four of the children who lived further away, became very good friends, because they came to school every day in the blue bus.

Joan was the first to get on the blue bus. She lived right on the edge of town. After a few bus-stops down the road, Paul and Mohammed also boarded the blue bus. After yet another stop, Sarah joined them. How excited the children were to meet their school friends again! They began to tell each other what they had been doing during the holidays.

Joan lived on a farm, so she told her friends about the beautiful baby horse, which had been born on her farm. She told them that the proper name for a baby horse was a "foal". Joan's father had promised that she could have it for herself as a present, if she worked hard at school.

Paul told his friends that he had received a lovely red and silver mountain bike for his birthday. It took him rather a long time to learn to ride it. Paul admitted he still felt nervous on the bike.

Then, Mohammed told the friends about his trip to France on a big ship called a "ferry". He said that the ship was so big that it could hold a thousand people, as well as cars, caravans, and trucks down below deck. The other children listened.

Now it was Sarah's turn to tell what had happened to her. Sarah was not smiling. Instead, there were big tears in her eyes. Sarah told them that on the day she came home from holiday, her Grandma had fallen down the stairs, and had broken her leg. Grandma was now in hospital. The other three children felt very sorry for Sarah. On the way home again in the blue bus, after school, the three happy children waited until Sarah had left the bus. Then they put their heads together and whispered about what they could do to make Sarah happy.

Next morning Joan, Paul, and Mohammed, were on the blue bus as usual. When Sarah boarded, the three children shouted out, "We have a present for you, Sarah!" They gave her a large bouquet of flowers. The children had gone home, and had asked their Mums and Dads, if they could pick some flowers from the garden to give to Sara's Grandma. "Give these flowers to your Grandma in hospital," they said. Sarah was smiling again. She thanked her three friends.

Sarah brought the flowers to Worship Assembly at the school that morning. The Headteacher allowed Sarah to read out the words on the little card, which was tied round the bouquet of flowers. She read out, "A good Friend always listens and tries to help." So Sarah took the flowers to Grandma that evening.

Grandma was delighted with them. On the blue bus next morning, Sarah told her friends all about it.

Prayer:

>   Teach us Lord, to value our friends, and to learn
>   that it is better to give, than to receive.
>   We thank you for nurses and doctors
>   who help to make us well again.
>   We give you our thanks for health. Amen.

Hymn:

>   Cross over the road. (C&P.l. 70)

Teachers' Note: This opening Worship Assembly lesson is based on the experience of children going back to school. The points to emphasise are, (1) School is a place where friends meet; (2) Friends share the joys and cares of life: (3) Friends learn to listen and help each other.

(b) Teachers are our Friends
Week 1   Friends

Today, I am going to ask you a very difficult question. I want you to think about it. "Which would be the better thing to do? To give a hungry man or woman a fish to eat, or to teach them how to catch a fish? (Some discussion may take place here.)

Ten children from a school went to visit Farmer Brown at Apple Tree Farm. Farmer Brown was a big friendly man. His face was tanned with the sun. He seemed to know everything about farming. He told the children to fill their pockets with as many apples as they wanted from his orchard. He showed them round the hen houses, and the duck pond.

Then he took them into a large barn. The hay, which the cows ate as food, was built high on one side of the barn. On the other side of the barn, the straw, which was used to make a bed for the cows, was also built high, right up to the roof. The children loved the red tractor which stood in the middle of the barn!

With a twinkle in his eye, Farmer Brown asked the ten children to go out into the field and catch his horse for him. He gave them a rope. The ten children ran after the horse, round and round the field. The horse was enjoying the fun too! He would stand still until the children were near, and then he would run off at a gallop. The children ran, and ran, until they were exhausted. They could not catch the horse.

Farmer Brown laughed, and asked the children to come outside the gate of the field. He said, "I'll show you how to catch a horse". Then he took a metal bucket, and put some oatmeal into it. He rattled the metal bucket against the gate. The horse pricked up his ears. Then to the children's amazement, the horse trotted over to the gate, and put his head into the bucket to eat the oatmeal. Farmer Brown quietly put a rope around the horse's neck, and smiled. "That is how to catch a horse," he said. The ten school children agreed that Farmer Brown would make a good teacher.

So let us go back to the question. " Which would be the better thing to do? To give a hungry man or woman a fish to eat, or to teach them how to catch a fish? The answer is, that it is better to teach them how to catch fish, because they can catch more fish, and feed themselves and their children for years to come. Farmer Brown could easily have caught the horse for the children, but he knew that-it was better to teach the children to do it for themselves. Then anytime they needed to catch the horse again, they would not need the farmer's help.

In this story Farmer Brown taught the children a new skill. He was a friend and a teacher. The teachers in school can also be friends. They know everyone's name. They know the things that children are good at, and ways in which they can improve their learning. They teach children how to help themselves. They show children how to learn many things. Let us say a prayer, and thank God for our teachers.

Prayer:
    Lord God, we thank you for our school friends.
    We thank you for our school teachers,
    because they care for us.
    and really are our friends.
    Help us to enjoy our work in school,
    and may we always do our best   Amen.

Hymn:
    Black and white. (C&P.1.67)

Teachers' Note: The emphasis today is, (1). that school is a place of learning. (2). that teachers as well as pupils may be friends of the children. (3). That children should try to do their best.

(c) Friends Together may Help   *Week 1 Friends*

Today, I am going to tell you two stories. One story comes from the Bible, and the second comes from the newspaper. I want you to listen carefully and to see if you can see any connections between the two stories.

Jesus was in a house which had a flat roof, The steps outside the house led up to the roof. The house was crowded full of people even at the door. No one could get in from the street. There was a sick man, in the village, who lay on a mattress all day long. This man had four good friends who believed that Jesus could heal the man, if only they could bring him near to Jesus.

The four friends carried the mattress with the sick man on it. Each of the four men held a corner of the mattress. They carried the mattress up the steps at the side of the house, and put it down on the flat roof.

They made a hole in the roof by removing some of the tiles. They tied a rope to each corner of the mattress, and lowered their sick friend down through the hole into the room. Everyone was amazed to see the man coming down through the roof. Jesus spoke to the man and healed him. The man feeling better, stood up, and carried his mattress away home with him.

Now for the second story. Mr. Jackson worked as an engineer on an oil rig in the North sea. An oil rig is a large steel platform, with great steel legs, which go deep into the sea. Sometimes the sea is so stormy, that large ships cannot go near the oil rig, in case the sea might cause them to crash against the steel legs. If that were to happen, then the ship, or the oil rig might sink.

One very stormy day, when huge waves were washing over the oil rig, Mr. Jackson felt ill. He had a terrible pain in his right side. The radio operator telephoned the Doctor on the shore, and told him about Mr. Jackson's pain. The Doctor said that Mr. Jackson, probably needed an operation at the hospital on the mainland.

On land the helicopter pilot, John, hurriedly started the engines, and his navigator Colin listened to the radio. He looked at a map of the North sea to find out the position of the oil rig. Then Doctor Wilson and Nurse Margaret, boarded the helicopter. It rose like a great noisy bird into the skies, and headed out over the stormy sea. Soon they were hovering in the air over the oil rig.

A very strong rope line was lowered from the helicopter. Mr Jackson was tied to the stretcher. He was pulled high up, into the air. The navigator, Colin, pulled Mr. Jackson inside the helicopter. Nurse Margaret, put a warm blanket around him, while Dr. Wilson felt his pulse. Quickly, pilot John turned the helicopter round. They carried Mr. Jackson over the rough sea to hospital, where he had his operation. Soon he was well again! It was only afterwards that Mr. Jackson realised that he had four good friends, whom he had never met before.

Children may come together to help someone in need. I am sure that you have seen several Scouts or Guides working together to wash a car. Children may join the junior section of St. John's Ambulance Brigade and learn First Aid. Thousands of children have become collectors for the National Children's Homes. Children, especially members of Youth Organisations may help to distribute the church Harvest fruit and flowers to the older people. They usually work together in parties of two or three, supervised by an adult.

6

Prayer:

Lord, help us to use our talents
to help someone in need.
Help us to learn worth-while skills
which will make us useful people,
and good friends in an emergency. Amen.

Hymn:

At the name of Jesus. (C&P.l. 58)

Teachers' Note: Reference is St. Mark Chapter 2. The Teacher asks the children what similarities they found in both stories. The four similarities which may be drawn out are. (1) Someone needing help. (2) Four active Friends. (3) Strong well-made ropes. (4) A place of healing.

(a) The "Titanic." *Week 2   Communications*

Schools are places where pupils learn how to communicate. One of the meanings of "Communication" is that of passing on information, or news to someone else. Newspapers, radio, and television are good examples. Can you think of any others? (Examples may be shown at this point.)

In the year 1912, the Titanic was the world's largest passenger liner. It was built in the Harland and Wolff shipyard, Belfast, Northern Ireland. The enormous ship measured 269 metres long. The Titanic had four funnels. It was designed to sail across the Atlantic ocean, from England to New York. Everyone believed that the Titanic was unsinkable, because it was divided up into compartments. Captain Smith on the bridge could work an electric switch, and bulkhead doors would close, making each compartment water-tight. Even if a large hole was accidentally made in four compartments, the ship would still keep afloat.

The Titanic sailed from Southampton on her maiden voyage, 10th. April 1912. Crowds cheered as she left the quayside. Some of the passengers were very rich, and others were poor. Everyone felt safe and secure. In the first class lounge, the orchestra provided music for the wealthy people, who danced late into the evening. The poorer people, looking forward to a new life in America, were in the third class section. There were children in every section of the ship.

The night of the 14th-15th April was clear and without fog. Another ship, named "Californian" had radioed the Titanic that there was a dangerous ice-field ahead. Then the California's radio operator turned off his radio. The sea was calm. A short time after that, a seaman on watch in the Titanic, peered out into the darkness, and suddenly he saw an ice-berg ahead of the ship. (Ice-bergs are at least twice as deep under the water, as they are in height above the water.) He rang the alarm bell three times. He then phoned officers on the bridge. They received the warning. The ship could not be stopped quickly, so instead the Titanic was turned to port, in an attempt to avoid the ice-berg. Instead of hitting the ice-berg head-on, the huge ship scraped alongside the ice. A long gaping hole, was torn in the side of five compartments. Water rushed in, and the Titanic slowly began to sink.

The radio operator sent out distress messages. The nearest ship, the "Californian " did not hear of the disaster, until the following morning, because her radio was turned off. Another ship, the "Carparthia" heard the calls for help, but she was farther away. When later, the "Carparthia" reached the scene, she was able to rescue 705 survivors, from the icy sea.

Including the crew, there were 2154 people on board, but the life-boats could only hold 1178. The life-boat rule at sea when an accident occurs, is "Women and children first." The brave seamen did their best, but there were not enough life-boats to save everyone from the water. The Titanic that night sank in two and a half hours. Approximately 1500 people were drowned. It was reported that before the ship sank, the orchestra on deck, played hymns to calm the frightened passengers.

No one realised that danger was so near. Later a Board of Trade enquiry was held to find the cause of the accident. A new regulation was passed, that all ocean ships must keep their radios on all the time. From that time onwards, ships had to have enough life-boats to take everyone on board.

The lesson we have to learn from the story of the Titanic is that clear communications are very important. As we write in class, we are learning to communicate with someone else. As we read, we are learning how to receive a communication. School is about learning how to pass messages to other people. Learn to do it well.

Prayer:

> We thank you Lord for the English language,
> and all other languages.
> We thank you for reading and writing.
> Help us to pass on good and wise messages,
> that will be a help to others.   Amen.

Hymn:

> I listen and I listen. (C&P.l. 60)

8

Teachers' Note: Points to make here. (1) The Titanic received a warning about ice ahead, from the "Californian". (2) It seems that the warning was not acted upon, until it was too late. (3) There was a shortage of life-boat places.

(b) Gossip

Week 2   Communications

Teachers' Preliminary Note: . To be effective, the following story must be told very slowly, and as if sharing a confidence. Allowing time between the different participant's gossip, will give the children time to see the obvious unfolding point. (1) Gossip can be very hurtful and cruel to people. (2) Gossip is a kind of spreading lies about people. (3) When we tell one lie in Gossiping, it seems to demand another lie to support it, and in doing so, the original information is no longer truthful.

There is another kind of communication called "gossip". When People talk to each other about someone they know, very often they add on to the information they already have, something more, which is not quite true. As the story is passed on between people it gets worse and worse. This happens because someone exaggerates. To "exaggerate" is to make a fact bigger than it really is.

(This story can be illustrated by asking nine children to stand in line at the front of the assembly; each child holding a large prepared name label representing the characters in the story. Just before the "punch" line, move Mrs. Jones from the first position to the last.)

Mrs Jones had a cold, so she stayed in bed that morning. Mrs Brown called to see her, and made her a cup of tea. Mrs. Jones happened to say that her leg felt a little stiff.

Mrs. Brown went down to the shop, and told Mrs. McNabb that she had been to see Mrs. Jones who was very ill in bed, with terrible pains in her leg.

Mrs. McNabb met Mr. Evans, the "lollipop man," at the traffic crossing and she told him that Mrs. Jones had fallen out of bed, and broken her leg.

Mr. Evans told the butcher's wife, Mrs. Potter, that Mrs. Jones had been knocked down by a bus, and that it had run over her leg.

Mrs. Potter told the Vicar's wife, Mrs. Watson, that Mrs. Jones was in hospital for an operation on her leg.

Mrs. Watson told the partly deaf green-grocer, John Field, that Mrs. Jones had her leg amputated in a hospital operation.

The green-grocer, John Field told a lady customer, Mary Hill, that Mrs. Jones was dying in hospital, after an operation.

Late that evening Mary Hill told her neighbour, Miss. Brooks, that Mrs Jones had died in hospital, after an operation on her leg.

Miss. Brooks could not keep the story to herself, and so next day she told a lady sitting on a seat in the park, that Mrs. Jones was dead. The lady in the park was very angry. She turned round to Miss. Brooks and said, "Don't be silly. I am Mrs. Jones.!"

Gossip is not always as silly as that! However, it is sometimes nearly as harmful. We must not tell lies about other people. On the other hand, there is such a thing as "good gossip" or conversation. When one of our school friends wins the chess competition, or when we hold a School concert, we have every right to spread the good news.

Prayer:

O Lord, help us to spread good news
about the people we know.
Let us not pass on unhelpful information.
Help us always to speak well of others.
May we learn to use words,
of encouragement and comfort.   Amen.

Hymn:

When I needed a neighbour. (C&P.l. 65)

(c) The Girl with a Good Message   *Week 2   Communications*

Bands of armed soldiers from Syria invaded the land of Israel. They over-ran the towns and villages, making the Israelite people prisoners. They compelled these prisoners to work as servants in the land of Syria. Among the people who were captured, was a little girl. We are not told her name.

She became a servant to the wife of a famous Syrian army officer, called "Naaman". The King of Syria was very pleased to have Naaman as a Commander over his army, because he was such a brave soldier. However, Naaman suffered from leprosy, which was a skin disease.

The little servant girl said to her Mistress one day. "If only my Master, Naaman, would visit the prophet Elisha, who lives in Samaria. Elisha could make him better!" Naaman hearing that someone could cure him, went to the King of Syria, to ask the King's permission to visit Israel.

The King of Syria wrote a letter of introduction to the King of Israel. "The man who brings this letter, is Naaman my good servant. I want you to cure him of his leprosy". Naaman also took presents of silver, gold, and ten changes of clothing.

When the King of Israel read the letter, he was afraid. He thought that the King of Syria was trying to make a quarrel between them, by asking him to heal Naaman. He said, "Am I a God, that I can kill, and give life again?"

When Elisha heard about it, he sent the King of Israel a message. "Send Naaman to me." Naaman arrived with his horses and chariots at Elisha's house. Elisha did not bother to meet Naaman. Instead, he sent a message. "Go and wash in the river Jordan seven times, and you will be healed."

Naaman was disturbed, because he expected that Elisha would come out and wave his hand over him, and call upon the Lord to heal him. He became very angry. Naaman thought that the rivers of Damascus in his own country, were better that the Jordan. He argued, "Can I not wash in them and be healed."

Naaman's servants pleaded with him. They said, "If the prophet had asked you to do some great thing, would you not have done it?" So Naaman paid attention to their wise advice. He dipped himself seven times in the Jordan. To everyone's surprise, Naaman was cured, and his skin became as healthy as a little child. Naaman offered Elisha presents, but he would not take them. Elisha spoke to Naaman, "Go in peace!" Naaman returned home accompanied by his servants, with their horses and chariots.

We must never forget the little servant girl, at the beginning of the story, who carried a good message about Elisha the Prophet. If she had been shy and kept quiet, Naaman would never have been healed.

Prayer:
> We thank you, Lord,
> for all who pass on good news.
> We thank you for the Post-men and Post-ladies,
> who deliver our letters;
> for Radio Operators, and the 999 service,
> who pass messages which are a means
> of helping sick people get well again.   Amen.

Hymn:
> Make me a channel of Your peace. (J.P. 161)

Teachers' Note: Reference; II Kings Chapter 5. The theme of carrying good news can be developed. (1) e.g. "Gospel" means "Good News". (2) The needs of the third world for hospitals, and skilled medical workers can be communicated into our homes by television. (3) We can help to heal people in the third world, by giving to charities, such as "Christian Aid" etc.

(a) The Mice and the Cat.

In the old barn the mice had a wonderful time. They had all the food, and warmth they needed. They loved to play about on the floor of the barn. Then a sad thing happened for the mice. The Farmer's wife brought home a lovely little black kitten. After a time it grew into a large black cat. The cat soon found out about the mice in the barn. He often would walk quietly into the barn, and pounce on one of the mice, and kill it. This happened so often, that the mice were becoming fewer in number. If matters were allowed to continue, soon no mice would be left. The problem was that the black cat never made a noise when he came in to the barn. He found the mice were very easy to catch.

The oldest and wisest of the mice decided to call a meeting of all the mice in the barn. When they met, they had a good debate about how to stop the cat catching their mice-friends. The mice chattered and made various suggestions. One smart young mouse stood up in the meeting and said, "Let us tie a blue ribbon with a bell on it, around the cat's neck. When the cat comes into the barn, we will hear the bell tinkle. We will know that he is there. That will give us time to run away into our holes." All the mice clapped their little paws. "What a splendid idea!" they shouted.

The wise old mouse, asked the meeting if they would vote on the proposal of tying a bell on a blue ribbon around the cat's neck. Every mouse, raised a little paw in agreement. Then the wise old mouse said, "Very good. I see that we are agreed on this matter. Now who is going to put the bell around the cat's neck?" The mice looked at each other, and they trembled inside their skin. One by one they slipped away into their holes, until not one mouse was left at the meeting! No mouse was willing to volunteer to put the bell around the cat's neck, because they were very frightened of being caught.

Many people are full of ideas about how to make things right. Yet when it comes to putting ideas into action, people excuse themselves. Many ideas are not very practicable. We must never be fool-hardy. Not many people want to be volunteers. Sometimes the only way to get action, is for someone to become a volunteer. To do that is a very brave thing to do. Leaders are often people who have that kind of character.

Prayer:

> Lord, make us wise, as well as brave.
> If there is a good task to do,
> and we believe that we can do it,
> then give each of us courage to be a volunteer.   Amen.

Hymn:
Have you seen the pussy cat, sitting on th wall? (J.P. 72)
or, All the animals. (C&P.2. 80)

Teachers' Note: Caution. There is a question of what is foolhardy, and what is wise. There is a certain danger in children volunteering for tasks beyond their capability. A good safe-guard for children is for them to ask advice from their parents, or teachers, before taking risks.

(1) The mice talked about the danger together. This is good! (2) The mice agreed together. Unity is usually a good thing. (3) The mice made the mistake of not being practical. (The idea would not work.)

(b) Rescued from the Fire.   *Week 3 Being Practical*

The Reverend John Wesley was an Anglican Minister. He is known more widely as the founder and leader of the Methodist societies. The Methodist Church has spread all over the world. We might never have had Methodist schools, hospitals and homes all over the world, were it not for the practical quick thinking of some unknown Lincolnshire villagers.

John Wesley was the eleventh child of the Rev. Samuel and Susanna Wesley. They lived in the Rectory at Epworth, near Doncaster. The Rev. Samuel Wesley was not liked by the villagers, because he condemned them for not attending church. One night, in 1703, the house caught fire. Some of the villagers may have deliberately set the Rectory ablaze. Fortunately, the family escaped from the blazing house. When they were outside, they realised that "Jackie, "as John was then called, had been left behind in the blazing building. At that time he was only five years of age.

An artist painted a picture of the scene of the fire. Outside the house there is a crowd of people. Some are filling buckets of water from the stream to put the fire out. Some are rescuing the horses from the stables. The family are huddled together outside. One boy is up a tree watching. The child, John, has been awakened by the noise, and the crackling of the flames in the roof. He puts his head out the window. The Father, the Reverend Samuel Wesley, is down on his knees praying that God might help his child to escape. There is no ladder, what can they do? Then a man in the crowd climbs on top of another man's shoulders. His arms reach out to the little boy, John, as he leans out of the open window. He brings the child down carefully. John has been rescued. The relieved Father gives thanks to God for the safety of his child.

John's mother, Susanna, believed that there must have been a purpose behind her child's escape from the flames. It was like a miracle. Her boy must be a chosen by God for some special task in the years ahead. "Is not this a brand plucked from the burning", Susanna said. John grew up, just as other boys do, but he was a serious boy. He too believed that God had a special purpose for his life. He never forgot his rescue from the flames. We must never forget the bravery of the two practical un-named rescuers. One who climbed on another man's shoulders, and the other man who held him up, to rescue a small boy.

Prayer:

> Help us to be careful not to cause fires.
> Teach us Lord to be practical and useful.
> We thank you for parents and teachers,
> who guard us from danger.
> We thank you for the life of John Wesley.   Amen.

Hymn:

> Light up the fire. (C&Pl. 55)

Teachers' Note: The story is a lesson for children to take care in a practical manner about causing a fire. (1) John Wesley had a good home. His mother was his first teacher. (2) John Wesley was only a young boy at this time. Boys and Girls are important to God, because they will be the future "grown-ups". (3) Ordinary people in the emergency saved John Wesley from the fire because they were practical people.

(c) Joseph the Practical Man.   *Week 3   Being Practical*

Sometimes a country goes through a difficult time in its history, and only a person of great practical skill and organisation can save the people from disaster. Joseph was a very practical person, as we shall see.

"Pharaoh" was the general name given to the Kings of Egypt. One night Pharaoh had a strange dream, and it really worried him. He dreamed that he was beside the river Nile, when seven fat cows came walking out of the river. They grazed among the reeds that grew there. Then to Pharoah's surprise, another seven thin ugly cows came out of the river, and ate up the seven fat cows.

Then Pharoah had a second dream. He dreamt that he saw seven ears of corn growing on one healthy stalk. Then he saw seven other thin ears of corn, which were scorched by the hot sun, grow up. They swallowed up the seven healthy full ears of corn. At once Pharaoh woke up from his strange dream. Pharaoh could not understand the dreams, but he felt sure that they had a meaning. So he sent for his magicians and asked them to explain the dream. None of them could interpret the dreams.

Pharaoh's chief cup-bearer (an old name for a Waiter who serves wine), heard about it. He went to the king, and said, "Pharaoh, I can remember when once you were angry with me, and put me in prison. While I was in prison I met a man by the name of 'Joseph' who could explain dreams." Pharaoh sent for Joseph to be brought before him. Pharaoh told Joseph his dreams.

Joseph knew the meaning. He explained that there would be seven years of good harvests and plenty of food for everyone. Then there would come seven years of poor harvests and famine, when people would go hungry. Pharaoh was so pleased, that he promoted Joseph to be second-in-command and ruler over Egypt. He gave Joseph his own signet ring. He put a gold chain around his neck. He gave him robes of the finest linen. Joseph rode through the streets in a chariot, pulled by horses.

Joseph ordered that during the seven years of plenty, all the corn should be stored-up in the cities. There was so much that it could not all be measured. Then when the seven years of poor harvests and famine came, the people pleaded with Pharaoh to give them food. He told the people to go to Joseph and ask for help. Joseph ordered that the storehouses should be opened, and everyone had a share of the corn to make bread. People even came from other lands to buy the grain. Joseph had saved the country from starvation, because he was a wise and a practical man. When his unkind brothers came to Egypt for food, he also sold it to them. Practical people are never wasteful people. They know how to save scarce materials. Are you practical?

Prayer:

> Lord, grant us the grace to give practical help
> to hungry people.
> Let us not always spend our money on ourselves.
> Teach us to share it with needy people,
> by giving to good causes.   Amen.

Hymn:

> Father lead me day by day. (J.P. 43)

Teachers' Note: The children can be assured that dreams are usually caused by what has happened in the past, and not by what is going to happen in the future. Reference, Genesis Chapter 41. (1) Joseph's idea was good; saving wheat and corn in years of plenty. (2) Joseph's skill was good; in practical organisation of store-houses beforehand. (3) Joseph's rationing of corn was good; there was enough for everyone when the famine came. In the past, Britain had to do this in war-time.

(a) The Final Push!

On a lonely hillside in Wales, Farmer Williams and his four sons worked hard on their farm. Three of the sons were grown men, and then there was David. He was only ten years old. David liked to help with the sheep, but he did not need to work as hard as the others, since he was only a boy.

Farmer Williams wanted to build another sheep shed to keep his flock in during the winter snows. The lambs which were born early, especially needed some warm shelter from the cold winds. He chose a good site on the mountain-side for such a building. The one snag was that a round-shaped enormous boulder-stone lay on the place, where they proposed to build the sheep-shed.

Farmer Williams thought hard about moving the stone. He took his tractor up the hillside and attached a chain from the tractor to the boulder-stone. When he started the engine, he found that the tractor wheels would not grip the clay soil on the hillside. The wheels kept going round, but the tractor did not move.

Farmer Williams felt that if he and his three sons could remove the soil under the stone, then they could give it a big push. It would roll down the mountain by itself, leaving a level site for the sheep building. They decided to begin digging. When they had cleared away the soil from underneath the great stone, it began to move a little forward and rolled back again.

Farmer Williams and this three strong sons, pushed the stone much more strongly. It began to move forward, but it always rolled back again. Young David was there, and he shouted, "Dad, can I come and help you?" "No", Farmer Williams shouted, "You had better stay away. Its too dangerous for a boy to be near." The four men pushed the stone with all their strength, but it always rolled back.

David pleaded, with his father and brothers, "Please, let me help! " At last they agreed that David could join them. David stood behind the stone with the other four men. "Ready, steady, push," they all said together ! It happened! The great stone began to move forward. David gave an extra push, and the stone rolled away down the mountain into the valley below. Farmer Williams could now build his sheep-shed on a level surface. The four men were laughing. They crowded around young David. "Thank you David," they said. "It was that last push that made all the difference." David thought to himself, "I have shown them that children can be useful." Farmer Williams felt very proud of his youngest son. David thought of an old saying. "Many hands make light work".

Prayer:

> Lord, It is good to be together.
> May we enjoy working with other people.
> Assist us always to do our best.
> Keep us from being lazy.   Amen.

Hymn:

> Give us hope, Lord. (C&P2. 87)

Teachers Note: (1) David was part of a family. (2) Even the youngest member of a family can be helpful. (3) David learnt that working with others gets the job done successfully.

(b) Social Habits.   *Week 4   Living Together*

Helen was a lovely girl, but she had some dreadful habits. In fact there were a number of children in school who were just like her. Helen often threw books down on the floor. In the morning she came to school late. Helen dropped litter everywhere she went. She opened doors, but never closed them behind her. Whenever Helen and her school friends went into a room, they often let the warm air escape through the open door. They thoughtlessly allowed cold draughts to blow into the room. They never closed the gates behind them in the fields, when they went for a walk. After they had passed through, the cows would later be found wandering on the busy road. In school Helen left the door of the rabbit hutch open, and the rabbits were found running about the playground. No-one liked Helen, or the other children who behaved like her, when they became careless and forgetful.

Mr. Turner the headteacher had spoken to Helen a number of times about her bad habits. Helen did not seem to care. At one morning Assembly, Mr. Turner decided to show Helen and the other children, that if they persisted in their behaviour, that after a time they would not be able to escape from their bad habits.

Mr. Turner called Helen up to the front of the Assembly. He took a large reel of cotton thread from his pocket. He asked Mrs. Brown, another Teacher, to tie it round Helen's arms and body once. He said, "Helen, try and break the thread." Helen easily broke the thread, and laughed. Mr. Turner, then asked the Teacher to tie the thread around Helen, three times, as the children were watching. Helen breathed in deeply, and pressed her arms out, and again she broke the thread. Although she felt that it was more difficult the second time.

Now, Mr. Turner asked the Teacher to tie the thread round and round Helen many times, as the children, sitting in silence, were beginning to understand the lesson. The headteacher said, "Helen, try and break the thread." Helen breathed very deeply, and she tried forcing her arms out-wards, but she could not move them. She was tied up as if with a strong rope. No matter how Helen tried, she could not break free. Immediately, the Teacher cut the thread with the scissors, and Helen became free and happy again. The children realised what had happened was like watching a school play being enacted before them. They wondered about its meaning!

Mr. Turner said to the children, "Imagine that every thread is one day. Children can break a bad habit if they only do wrong a few times. However, if they are bad every day, then after months of bad behaviour, they will find that they are unable to escape from their bad habits. The bad ways take over, and it becomes almost impossible to be good." They understood, because really underneath, they were good children. Helen made up her mind to be very careful in future. She took care of books. She came to school early, and felt so much better about attending school. Helen helped the other children to pick up their litter and to put it into litter bins. She really tried to close gates and doors behind her. Everyone began to like Helen and they became her friends again. When the Teacher was in the playground, and she wanted a responsible person to take care of her keys, whom do you think she chose? The most amazing thing was that the other children who had copied Helen's bad habits, now copied her good one's. The school became a much happier place.

Prayer:

> Teach us Lord, to be considerate of others.
> Let not bad habits bind us.
> Show us that actions form habits,
> and that habits form our character.
> Help us to form good habits.   Amen.

Hymn:

> He made me. (C&Pl. 18)

Teachers' Note: (1) Helen had some bad habits. (2) She may not have been aware of her bad habits. (3) Acts form habits, and habits form character. (4) Everybody liked Helen. when she changed her conduct.

(c) **Being a Good Example**

The roads that Jesus and his disciples walked were not in the least like our roads. There had no tar-macadam surface on them, and no drains at the side of them to take away the rain. Instead, they were either dusty stone tracks, or in wet weather they became wet muddy paths. People in those days only wore sandals. It was the custom for householders to provide a bowl of water and a towel to wash the dirty feet of visitors who came to their home. If the home had a servant, then the servant would kneel down, wash and dry the visitor's feet. This action was considered to be very good manners.

After a journey, Jesus and his disciples arrived at the house with the large upper room. No servant met them at the door to wash the feet of the guests. Who was going to do the feet washing? Each one of the disciples was too proud to stoop down before the others and act like a servant. After they had the meal in the upper room, Jesus took a towel and a basin of water. He knelt down, and washed the feet of each of the disciples.

Jesus then asked the disciples, if they understood what he had just done. He said, " You call me Master and Lord, that is good. If I have washed your feet, you ought to wash each other's feet. I have set you a good example. If you know these things, you will be happy if you do them."

Now for a second story. It was Wendy's Birthday. Her mother provided a garden party for fifteen of Wendy's school friends. It was a beautiful garden, surrounded by trees and full of brightly coloured flowers. The Summer day was very warm and dry. There were plenty of good things on the long table. Cake, chocolate biscuits, ice cream, lemonade, and other delicious food to eat. After the party was over, the children declared that had been a great success. They continued to play games in the garden.

Now Wendy's mother was a widow, since Wendy's father had died the previous Year. She had no husband to help with the washing up. Neither had she a dish washer. After the party, in the kitchen there were such a large number of used cups, plates, jelly and ice cream dishes, knives and spoons waiting to be washed up.

Four of the children looked into the kitchen. "Let us help Wendy's Mother wash up", they said. As the eleven others were playing games in the garden, the four children helped Wendy's mother wash and dry every one of the dirty dishes. They did not drop a cup or a plate. Wendy's Mother smiled at the four children. "Thank you children," she said, "You are a good example, and have been very kind to me today, just when I needed help."

Can you see that both of these stories teach a similar lesson? We must learn to serve each other. If we only look after ourselves, then we become selfish people.

Others will soon find out if you are selfish and only interested in yourself. There is a saying, "Do unto others as you would want them to do unto you." You could ask yourself the question.

"If everyone in our school were just like me?
What kind of a school would our school be?"

Prayer:

Teach us Lord, the pleasure of being helpful.
Let us not be so taken up by ourselves,
that we forget the work we make
for our Parents and Friends.
Make us thoughtful and useful people.   Amen.

Hymn:

When Jesus walked in Galilee. (C&Pl. 25)

Teachers' Note: The Bible story is taken from St. John 13. Points to stress here are; (1). The Disciples were too proud to act as the servant. Sometimes pride in ourselves has to be conquered in order to help others. (2) Serving strangers may be easy, but serving those whom we know may be the most difficult task of all. (3) Jesus set us a good example.

(a) "Harvest" Means an Increase   *Week 5   Harvest*

Old John was a retired railwayman. He lived in a country village. His small cottage had a field behind it. Old John never used his field very much. He was driving home one day in his car, when he spotted five potatoes lying in the middle of the road. They, perhaps, had fallen off a tractor, or a lorry. He turned off the car engine. Getting out, he picked up the five potatoes, and took them home with him.

Old John kept the potatoes in a paper bag, and the next Spring, he planted the five potatoes in a row, in his small field. The following September he dug the potatoes up, and found that he now had thirty large potatoes, and some very small ones. Again, he kept the potatoes until the following Spring. He planted his thirty potatoes, in another part of the field. (Farmers always rotate their crops.) The next September, Old John dug up his potatoes, and this time he counted one hundred and fifty potatoes.

The third year he planted all his potatoes, and at the end of the season, he dug up nearly eight hundred potatoes. Old John, now thought to himself. "If I plant all these for the fourth year, then I will have enough to sell, and enough to keep as seed". Sure enough, they had a wet year that year, and the potatoes grew very quickly during the rainy weather. He had a bountiful Harvest. He packed most of his potato crop in bags, and sold them to a shop in the town. He kept enough back for himself to use next Spring.

With the money gained from selling the potatoes, Old John was able to send a cheque to some missionaries who were helping poor farmers in Africa. The missionaries who received the cheque bought maize seed with it. They gave the maize seed to a number of local farmers. The farmers planted it in their fields. The following year it was a good harvest. The poor African farmers had enough to eat, and enough to keep as seed.

This harvest story all began with someone with a kind heart finding five potatoes. God has so planned our world, that there is enough food for everyone if it is shared out properly. The Harvest usually means an increase of wheat, corn, barley, maize, fruit, and nuts. Increased Harvests mean that people will not die of hunger. The money they gain from selling their Harvest, can be used to buy warm clothing, or other goods which they need for their homes.

Prayer:

We are amazed, Lord, at the Harvest.
We are grateful that seed can grow and increase.
Thank you Father, for sunshine and rain,
for fields, and good soil.
Thank you, Lord, for farmers
who work so hard in the fields,
to provide us with food.   Amen.

Hymn:

Pears and apples. (C&P.2. 135)

Teachers' Note: (1)) Harvest depends on good seed. Harvest depends on human labour in the fields, suitable weather, and careful reaping and storing. (2) Harvest was meant to be shared and enjoyed by all. (Old John had a kind heart). (3) Harvest is a good time to say "Thank You" to God.

(b) Harvest Depends on Water.   *Week 5   Harvest*

In one of the areas of the United States of America, where they grow vast acres of Wheat, there was a drought. The rain had not fallen for a long time, and it looked as if the growing wheat was going to die in the fields. The farmers were very worried about the lack of rain. They decided to call all the people in the countryside to meet in the church on the Sunday to pray for rain. That week the sun still shone down on the fields, and still the rain did not come. The farmers knew that if the rain did not come at the right time of the year, that the wheat plants would produce a very poor Harvest.

When Sunday arrived all the farmers came to Church with their sleeves rolled up. Their wives and daughters also came in their sun dresses, because it was so hot and dry. They were amused to see a little girl of nine years of age arrive at church that morning. She was dressed in her rain-coat and plastic rain-hat. She also carried an umbrella.

They smiled at the little girl, and laughed at her wearing a rain coat. The little girl listened to the Farmers and their Wives singing the hymns. Then she heard the Minister praying for rain to make the wheat grow. The little girl also prayed for rain. Everyone said "Amen" to the Minister's prayer, but no-one heard the little girl's prayer, except the Lord himself.

The church service ended, and the congregation made their way home. As they left a great black cloud suddenly appeared in the sky. There was a rumble of thunder, and the rain came down in torrents. Of course, the farmers who were without their coats, and their wives who were wearing their sun dresses were drenched by the rain, long before they reached their homes One little girl just smiled to herself, as she put up her umbrella. "Thank you", Lord, she said. She believed her prayer had brought the rain.

The Bible tells us about a Prophet called Elijah who prayed, and the rain stopped, and he prayed three years after, and the rain came. There are some people who believe that God can intervene and change the weather. When the Spanish Armada (a large fleet of sailing warships) set sail to invade England, in the sixteenth century, a great storm arose and wrecked most of their ships. People said that storm was an act of God, which saved England. Just as some people thought that when York Minister caught fire that God must have been angry.

We cannot really influence the weather by our prayers. If we could change the weather by our prayers, then we would all pray that the droughts in Africa would stop. The people there would have rain on their dry and dusty lands. The poor people would be able to grow crops in their fields for food and no-one would die from starvation. That does not happen. Praying does not make the rain come. Rain depends on the climate of a country.

In Britain, growing crops depend on the early rain fall. Rain is life to plants. Without rain, there can be no Harvest. When we are about to go away on holiday, and we hope for good dry weather, we must not forget that the farmers, and the market-gardeners may be hoping for rain. Which is the more important; someone having a dry holiday, or the growing crops having a good shower of rain?

God has put us in a wonderful world. We thank God for the rain. In our own homes we use large amounts of water. Sometimes we may even waste water. When we are short of rain in England, we are grateful for places like the Lake District, and the Kielder Reservoir, where water is conserved until it is needed. Harvest also needs the sunshine. So we are thankful for both the rain and the sunshine.

Prayer:

> We thank you, God, for refreshing rain.
> We are grateful for the pleasant Summer sun.
> We pray for Farmers and Market Gardeners,
> and everyone who looks for a good harvest.
> Grant them success in their endeavours.
> Father God, give us your peace.   Amen.

Hymn:

> You can't stop the rain from falling down. (JP. 297)

Teachers' Note: (1) The farmers in the story worked well. They expected to plough, sow, and reap the wheat. (2) Sometimes we expect our prayers to change the weather just for our convenience. When we pray this we we are forgetting the need of rain for farming. (3) We ought not to waste water. We ought to be thankful for places like the Lake District, or the Kielder Reservoir.

(c) The Harvest of the Sea.   *Week 5   Harvest*

Sometimes when we visit a church beside the docks, we see that the pulpit is shaped like the prow of a ship. This reminds us that once, Jesus was by the seaside, when a large crowd of people came to hear him speak. He boarded one of the fishing boats, which was pushed out a little from the shore. From that position in the boat, Jesus taught the people, who were on the shore.

Jesus then said to Simon Peter, "Let us go out into the deep water. You can let down your nets, and catch some fish. Simon said to Jesus, "Teacher, we have already been out fishing all night, but we could not catch any. However, you have asked us, so we will try again."

They let down their nets as Jesus had told them to do. There were astonished at the great number of fish in the nets. The nets began to break from the weight of fish. They called for help to their partners who were in the other ship. Soon both ships were filled with fish. Simon Peter fell down on his knees before Jesus, to thank him. From that time onwards, the brothers, Simon Peter and Andrew, and the second pair of brothers, James and John became followers and friends of Jesus. They left their nets behind them, and no longer worked as fishermen.

We are making a mistake if we think of Harvest as only being the food grown on land. There is also a harvest of the sea. Oysters, shell fish, crabs, lobsters, as well as fish, supply the people of the Earth with food. Everyone in this Assembly must have enjoyed a meal of fish (and chips) at some time!

How many kinds of fish can you name? (Here the Teacher may ask the children to name the fish they know. Some will be fresh water fish, and others are found in salt water.) Did you know that many years ago, the early Christians were persecuted by the Romans? The Christians used to hide in the underground catacombs for safety. (Underground tunnels for burying the dead.) They had a secret sign, the "sign of the fish," which was found chalked on the walls of the catacombs, hundreds of years afterwards. The Greek word for "Fish" is spelt "Ichthus". Each letter of "Ichthus" had a secret meaning. The letters meant "Jesus Christ Son of God." The "sign of the Fish" was just as important as the "Sign of the Cross" which we can see in our churches today.

Prayer:

Thank you, Lord for the Harvest of the sea.
Bless the brave fishermen who sail in ships,
and provide us with our fish and sea-food.
Encourage us to protect our environment,
and to keep the sea clean for sea creatures.
When on holiday, may we leave our beaches clean and tidy.   Amen.

Hymn:

Think of a world without any flowers. (C&P.l. 17)

Teachers' Note: The story has to be correlated with accounts of the calling of the Disciples in Matthew 4, Mark 1, and Luke 5. (1) Even in Bible days people needed the Harvest of the Sea for food. (2) The account need not necessarily be a miracle. Jesus could have seen the Gulls over the place where the shoal was swimming. (3) Because the sea provides food, we must try to keep the sea clean.

(a) **Working in the Dark**

A party of students wanted to see an underground colliery. A colliery is a place where coal is mined. They made an arrangement to visit a Scottish Coal Pit. They arrived at the Pit-head office, where the Manager welcomed the party. He asked each of the student- visitors to sign a form, which meant that those who went down coal pit, went down at their own risk. The Colliery was not be held responsible for any accidents to the visitors.

The students were each given a miner's helmet, which had a lamp on the front of it. They also received an electric battery on a belt, to be fitted around their waists. A connecting wire was attached from the belt to the helmet light.

An experienced coal miner led the party to the "Cage." This was a lift just like a cage, which would hold about fifteen people. Whenever anyone visits a coal-pit they see a great wheel, high up, above the wheel- house. In the wheel-house, there is a man who operates the cables which lower the cage to the bottom of the pit-shaft. He speaks by telephone to a second operator who is at the bottom of the shaft. This second operator's task is to open the cage door, when people arrive at the bottom. When the winding wheel turns at the top, the cage is either going up, or down.

The students in the cage went down so fast, that they felt as if they were going upwards. The operator opened the cage door, and let everyone out. The students followed the leading Miner along a well-lit underground road, which went for about a mile. The road was really a railway track. Small wagons full of coal were going one way, and empty wagons were going the other way. A coal pit is very like a rabbit warren, with plenty of burrows off the main road through the rocky ground.

The faces of all the miners who worked below ground were blackened with the coal dust. The leading Miner now turned to the left to go up a smaller side road. He asked the students to switch on the lights on their helmets, because there were no lights on the side roads. Nothing could be seen. Everything was blackness. The roof of the side road was only about one and a quarter metres high, so everyone had to stoop hunched up, as they moved forward to the coal face. The "coal face" is where the coal-cutting machinery digs out the coal, which is carried on belts, to be emptied into the wagons on rails.

Just before the party reached the coal face, the leading Miner said. "Now, fellows, I want you all to switch off the lamps on your hats". Everyone did as they were told. It was utter darkness. "Try and look at your fingers", the Miner said, in the blackness. No one could see anything. Some of them became very frightened in the darkness. Then the Miner said something which the students never forgot. He said, "This is what it is like to be blind." They all understood. To be blind was never to be able to see the daylight, or anything else. They all switched on their lights again, and went back to the cage.

They enjoyed their visit to the colliery, but they had learned something about blindness which they never forgot. The cage took them up to the world of green fields again. Some of the students were thinking to themselves and were very quiet. They now understood blindness a little better. They also understood why the Miners love the clear blue sky, and the shining sun.

We ought to be thankful to God that he has given us good eye-sight. We can see the lovely flowers, and the faces of our friends. We can look up at the birds, or enjoy reading books. There are many blind children in the world. Doctors do their best to help them. Sometimes blind people carry a white walking-stick to let others know they are blind. This stick is useful, walking along a pavement, and especially when crossing the road. Many blind people have a guide dog with very good eyesight, to guide their owners. Blind people want to be treated as if they were sighted people, but sometimes they need our help.

Prayer:

> We thank you Lord, for our eyesight.
> We can see and enjoy so many beautiful things.
> We thank you for the blue of the sky;
> and the green of the fields and hedges.
> Bless all blind people, and their guide dogs.   Amen.,

Hymn:

> All things bright and beautiful. (C&P.l. 3)

Teachers' Note: Story points. (1) We are not to be afraid in the dark. (2) We ought to thank God for our eye-sight. We ought to thank God for our beautiful world of colour. (3) We need not pity blind people, because we are, "sighted". Blind people resent pity, because they want to be treated just like the rest of us. Blind people develop other faculties, especially memory and the ability to listen.

(b) A Blind Person's Best Friend   *Week 6   Blindness*

Mr. Shaw was not blind himself, but he voluntarily worked for a Centre which trained suitable dogs to help Blind people. He had heard that Farmer Burn's beautiful Labrador bitch had a litter of five pups. He travelled down by car, to meet Farmer Burns. "I hear that you have five new pups on your farm," Mr. Shaw said. Farmer Burns smiled, "Yes", he said, "they are all little beauties."

Mr. Shaw said,"I want you to sell me the best pup of the litter. I want it for a very special reason." Farmer Burns allowed Mr. Shaw to see the six week old pups as they cuddled up to their mother dog. Both men decided which was the strongest of the pups, and agreed that Mr. Shaw would come back in another six weeks time to collect the pup. They decided to call the pup, "Beauty" because she really was beautiful.

Mr. Shaw came back again when the pup was three months old. He took her home, because he wanted Beauty to learn to live with human beings. At first Beauty did what all pups do. She chewed the slippers, and the legs of the chairs, because her new teeth and gums were sore. However, she soon stopped that, as she grew older. Mr. Shaw took Beauty everywhere he went, even to church on Sunday. The pup grew up into a very strong intelligent and obedient dog.

A sad day came for Mr. Shaw when he took Beauty to the Training Centre in order to be trained as a Guide Dog for the Blind. He loved Beauty, but he knew that Beauty was a special dog, and that they had to part. Beauty had to be trained by expert dog trainers to be able to guide a blind person. She was to become some blind person's special friend. So they parted company.

Beauty was so clever and intelligent that she soon learned to stop at road kerbs, when to stand, and when to sit down. She never ran after cats, or other dogs in the street. She could sit through a church service without disturbing anyone. At the end of her long training she was now ready for her special task in life. A man who had been blind from when he was a boy was introduced to Beauty. He was allowed to take Beauty home. The dog and the blind man became good friends. Beauty guided her new master everywhere he went, and because she was a special dog, she was the only dog allowed to walk round the super-market, when her Master needed to buy his groceries.

A few months went by, and Mr. Shaw went down to see Farmer Burns again. Can you guess why?

Prayer:

Father God, we thank you for the Training Centres,
where Guide Dogs for the Blind,
are trained to be friends of blind people.
We thank you for those kind people,
who are interested in helping the Blind.   Amen.

Hymn:

He made me. (C&P.1. 18)

Teachers' Note: Children are interested in charities for the blind. (1) Dogs have differing personalities, just as people have differing temperaments. They are specially chosen. (2) Dogs may stay with selected people for about one year before training. (3) Dogs learn to become work dogs rather than pet dogs at a

Training Centre. Their eyes become a Blind person's eyes. A deep friendship and understanding grows between Master or Mistress and the dog.

(c) A Blind Man Sees Again!   *Week 6   Blindness*

Saul of Tarsus was a very religious person. In those days people were very cruel. They did not like the Christians. One day a Christian man named Stephen was being stoned to death outside the walls of Jerusalem. The people who were throwing the stones took off their coats, and Saul looked after them. Saul spent his time persecuting Christians in the area, and putting them into prison.

One day Saul was travelling to the city of Damascus with soldiers. He carried a letter of authority that gave him the power to arrest any Christians he found there. He intended to capture Christians, and bring them back in chains to Jerusalem. As he walked down the Damascus road, suddenly, a dazzling light flashed upon him. Saul was thrown to the ground. A voice said, "Saul, why are you persecuting me? I am Jesus". The soldiers along with Saul could hear the voice, but they could not see anyone. Saul said, "What shall I do? " The voice answered, "Go into Damascus and wait there. You will be told what to do."

When Saul stood up again. He could not see anything. He had been blinded by the light. They took Saul to a house in Straight street, in Damascus. For the next three days Saul did not eat. Worse still, he could not see. Then the Lord said to a Christian man in Damascus, named Ananias, "Go to the house of Judas in Straight Street, and ask for Saul of Tarsus. He is praying at this moment." Ananias was frightened, because he knew how Saul persecuted the Christians. He said, "Lord,I have heard all about this man. He puts Christians in Prison. That is why he is here in Damascus."

The Lord said, "Go and pay Saul a visit. He has been chosen by me as a special messenger. He will carry my message to the Jewish people, and to the Gentile people. He will even speak to Kings. Ananias went to the house in Straight Street. When Ananias met Saul, he addressed him as "Brother Saul". Ananias then put his hands on Saul's head. He told him that the Lord Jesus had sent him to cure him of his blindness, and that Saul was to receive the power of the Holy spirit. Immediately, Saul was cured of his blindness, and he received the new power in his life. He was then baptised in water as a sign that he was now a Christian. From that time onwards, Saul was known by the name of "Paul". He became a faithful Minister of the Lord Jesus. He formed people into churches everywhere he went.

Prayer:

> Lord, we thank you for the Apostle Paul,
> who stopped persecuting other people.
> We are glad that his blindness was cured.
> Bless all blind people:
> Teach us to be kind to everyone.   Amen.

Hymn:

> His name was Saul of Tarsus. (JP. 363)

Teachers' Note: (1) Saul was religious but not very kind. We must never hate anyone because of their religion. (Ananias, the Christian, welcomed Saul, as "Brother Saul!") (2) Saul was blind for only three days. Many people are blind all their lives. (3) Today, hospitals still cure many blind people. Doctors are continuing the healing work of Jesus. Thank God for Opticians.

(a) The Lost Boat   *Week 7   Crafts-people*

Everyone is good at something. Everyone has a talent. It may be that you are good at one of the following activities; football, hockey, music, drawing, knitting, running, writing, climbing, swimming, dancing, gardening, collecting things, operating computers, cycling, reading, or sewing.

Tom was good at working with wood. He lived beside the sea. He had no toys of his own, because he was very poor. He used to collect old wooden boxes and pieces of wood which had been washed up on the beach. He took them home, and made his own toys. Tom was very clever with his hands. He made a beautiful sailing ship, just like one of the old ships that he saw anchored in the harbour.

The ship was special to Tom, because it took him so long to make it. He had to carve out the shape from a large piece of wood. He worked in a shed behind the cottage. Finally, Tom made the masts and the sails, and then painted the ship blue and white. He tied a piece of string to the prow of the sailing ship, and decided to try it out in the inner harbour, where the water was calm The blue ship sailed beautifully, as the sea breeze caught the sails. Last of all, Tom decided to give his ship a name, because all sailing ships had a name. He named his ship the "Sea Queen". It took another day or two to paint the name on the side of the model ship.

Tom was very proud of his ship. He would often talk to it. He would say, "I made you, and I love you." Tom took his ship to the harbour every day after school, and had a lot of fun sailing it. One rather windy day, Tom decided to try to sail his ship in the real sea, outside the harbour wall. He let the string attached to the "Sea Queen" become longer and longer. The "Sea Queen" caught the wind, and sailed out quite a distance. Then something dreadful happened. The string broke, and the wind carried the little ship far out to sea. Tom was heart broken. He went home in tears, saying to himself, "I made you: I loved you; and I've lost you!"

The weeks went by. Tom searched the shore each day, but to no avail. One day, Tom was walking along the main street of the fishing village. He looked into the window of a second-hand shop. He was overjoyed. There it was! The blue sailing ship, with the words, "Sea Queen" written on the bow, was in the shop window. Tom rushed into the shop, and said to the shop-keeper, "I want my boat back." The Shop-keeper replied, "That ship is mine. I bought it from a fisherman, who told me it became caught in his nets. If you want that ship then you will need to pay me, one half crown for it." (Half crown was a coin used in those days before decimal currency was introduced. The coin was worth twelve and a half pence in today's money.)

Tom ran home, sat down and began to think to himself, how he could earn a half crown, which was made up of thirty "old kind" of pennies. Everyone used coal or wood fires in those days. Smoke came out of all the chimneys. Tom began to collect all the old wood he could find. He took a small axe, and chopped the wood into firewood and sold it around the houses in the village. Everyone needed fire-wood, so they paid Tom, one penny per bundle.

Next day after school, Tom ran down to the shop, with thirty pennies in his hand. "Please, can I have my "Sea Queen" now," he said. The shop-keeper counted out the thirty pennies. "Yes", he said, "Thirty pennies add up to a half crown." He handed the model ship to Tom. Tom ran all the way home. He was clutching his ship, and saying, " I made you, I loved you, and I lost you.......I found you, I loved you, and I bought you......Now you are twice mine! " He was the happiest boy in the village. He showed his "Sea Queen " to all the children in the village school and the Teacher allowed the children to draw the ship. If they could not make a ship, at least they could all draw one.

Prayer:

> Lord we thank you for crafts and skills.
> May we use what talents we have,
> and as we create some new thing,
> may we really care about what we do.
> Make us good creators.
> Teach us to love beautiful objects.   Amen.

30

Hymn:

The building song. (C&P.l. 61)

Teachers' Note: (1) Our Talents are a gift from God to use in a good manner. (2) To love beautiful things, such as the sea, music, nature, sculpture, or colours, is good. (3) Tom lost his model ship but he never gave up hope. He worked hard to buy the ship back. God loves children to put their best into any task they do.

(b) Michelangelo Sculptor and Painter   *Week 7   Crafts-people*

Long ago, in the year 1474, in the town of Caprese, in Tuscany, Italy, a baby was born. This baby was the second son of the Mayor of the town. It was the custom in those days, that the baby of rich people, or business people, was placed in the care of Foster Parents for the first few years. The baby, Michelangelo, was put into the care of a poor stone-mason and his wife. So from his boyhood days, Michelangelo had become accustomed to the sound of his Foster-father cutting the stone with his hammer and chisel. The child was very interested in art. He had a deep love for sculpture and painting. At that time there were many statues and paintings to be seen in Italy, especially in the churches, and in the houses of the rich people.

When the young boy, Michelangelo, reached school age, he went to live with his own parents. They had moved to the city of Florence, which was the leading city in the world of art. Michelangelo did not like school very much. The one subject he was really good at was drawing. He seemed to be drawing or painting pictures at every opportunity. His father wanted him to be a learned scholar, so he took the pencils and paint brushes away from Michelangelo, to help him pay more attention to his other lessons.

Nevertheless, the young boy could not resist any opportunity to paint, or chisel stone. One day his father looked at a painting by Michelangelo, copied from another artist's original painting. He was amazed at the boy's talent, and changed his mind about his son's future. He sent him to a studio in Florence to work as an apprentice painter. The Master of the studio was a well known artist by the name of Ghirlandajo.

There was a time when Michelangelo heard excited people in the street talking about a famous Preacher, Savanarolo, who had visited the area. He decided to go and hear him. Savanarolo would sometimes preach in the churches, and sometimes outside in the market places. What Savanarolo said about people obeying the Word of God had a deep effect on Michelango's mind. He determined that in future his painting and sculpture should always carry a meaning and message, just like any preacher who preached a sermon from the

Bible. Michelangelo's paintings appear to be real people out of the Bible. This was very helpful to the ordinary people who often could not read, and lived before television was invented. He made the Bible come alive (in their minds).

When Michelangelo was twenty-one years of age he left the city of Florence, to go the larger city of Rome. His first masterpiece was the painting of Mary, the mother of Jesus, holding him close in her arms after he had died on the cross. Another famous work by Michelangelo was a a statue of the David, another figure out of the Bible which he carved out of stone, nearly four metres high. He made the statue for the city of Florence. Most people of those days judged Michelangelo to be the best sculptor in the world.

In the year 1512 Michelangelo was appointed to paint beautiful pictures on the ceilings and walls of the Sistine Chapel in Rome. It took four years for him to complete all the paintings. Before he began to paint, he ordered that high wooden scaffolding should be built inside the chapel, high up near the ceiling. In order to paint the pictures on the ceiling, Michelangelo had to lie on his back every day. He lay painting through-out four years, working often with the paint dripping on his face. He painted nine pictures of the creation of the world. On one wall he painted a painting of "The Last Judgement." Today, anyone who goes to Rome may visit the Sistine Chapel, and see these beautiful paintings.

When Michelangelo died, the Church authorities held a special funeral service for the famous sculptor and painter. An enormous crowd filled the, "Church of the Apostle Saints" in the city of Rome. People held him in great honour because they admired the skill shown in his beautiful pictures and statues.

Prayer:

> Teach us Lord to use our skills and crafts
> in school and in the world.
> If we are good at some kind of art,
> then show us how to use our work,
> for the interest of others,
> and to the glory of God.   Amen.

Hymn:

> Somebody greater. (C&P.l. 5)

Teachers' Note: (1) Any child early or later may show creative skills. (Knitting, sewing, drawing, painting, modelling with clay, wood, metal, or plastic. (2) Every piece of art carries a meaning. (3) We all may make things to give pleasure to parents and Friends. Even Pupils may create articles to the glory of God.

32

(c) **Builders**

Jesus often told stories. He once told the people about two builders. Both of them decided to build themselves a house each. Maybe they were being married at the same time, and needed a new home. There were plenty of stones lying around, so it was easy to get the materials for building. Now the important part of any house is the part underneath that we do not see, after the house has been built. It is named the "foundation". Every house has to be built on something. Nowadays, they usually mix concrete and pour it into the ground, and wait until it hardens. Then they build the brick walls upon the concrete.

The first builder was a very wise builder. He chose to build his house on solid rock. So the foundation underneath, although it could not be seen, would never move. He soon built up the walls on top of the rock, leaving spaces for light to come into the room, because they did not usually have glass windows in those days. Soon he had finished the roof, to keep out the rain. The house looked lovely, and so he began to live in it.

The second builder was not a very wise builder. He did not like digging out hard rock. Instead he chose a sandy place, which would be much easier to dig out. Then he began to build the walls, and he also left spaces in the walls to act as windows. He soon had built the roof on top of the walls. To tell the truth, if anyone looked at the two houses, after they were built, one house appeared to be just as good as the other one. The second builder also moved into his new house.

Both houses looked splendid in the warm days, as the sun shone down upon them. Both builders were very satisfied with their work. Some time afterwards a storm arose, and the winds blew, and the water came rushing past the house, just as we sometimes see on the television news. The house which was built on the rock foundation stood strong and firm. It could not be moved, because it was built upon a rock.

The rain, and wind also beat upon the house that was built upon the sand. Everyone in school knows that when sand gets wet it moves. (Children know that sand moves when they leave their foot-prints on wet sand at the seaside.) The rain poured down, and it became a torrent of water, rushing down the street and past the house. The sand foundations underneath the walls began to move. All at once there was a loud crashing sound as the house built upon the sand fell down. The second builder realised that he had been a very foolish man.

Jesus said that the meaning of the story was, that people who did not listen to his message were like the foolish man. People who obeyed the words of Jesus would be safe, like the man who built his house on the rock. They would be safe in the storms of life.

Foundations are not seen, but they are important. No one will see your honesty, truthfulness or kindness, but these qualities will be an unseen foundation inside you, making you a strong and upright person.

Prayer:

> Lord, we are all builders in life.
> Our life is like a house.
> Help us to lay a good foundation.
> May we build up our lives
> upon goodness, honesty, kindness,
> and faith in God.
> Assist us to love fair play.
> Make us try to be good scholars;
> or good at making things; or good at music;
> or good at sport, or some other skill.   Amen.

Hymn:

> The wise man built his house upon the rock. (JP. 252)

Teachers' Note: (1) Both builders worked hard. We give good points for difficult and skilled work. (2) Both Houses looked lovely when they were finished. People look alike from the outside appearance. It is unseen things like kindness, honesty, truthfulness that are important because they are the foundations of our lives. (3) Days are like bricks or stones in a house. We add to our own self-building everything we do. That is why it is helpful to practise sports, music, schoolwork, and good deeds.

(a) The Scarred Hands   *Week 8   Hands*

Fiona had grown into a beautiful girl of ten years of age. Indeed she and her mother looked very like each other. One day at dinner, she was talking to her mother. She said, "Mummy, I think you are a wonderful Mum. You are the best Mum in the whole world! I like your hair, and I love your face. I like your brown eyes, Mummy." Fiona stopped talking for a moment, then she took a deep breath, and she said, "But Mummy I hate your hands!"

Fiona looked down at her mother's hands. They were rough, and badly scarred, especially on the back of them. Fiona thought they looked ugly.

Mother sat down beside her growing daughter, and said, "Come Fiona, and I'll tell you all about my scarred hands."

"Once upon a time, I lived in another house. There was a tiny baby girl lying fast asleep in the cot, in an upstairs room. The little baby was small and helpless, yet she looked so beautiful, as she lay asleep. I went downstairs, and sometime afterwards, I could smell smoke coming from upstairs. I rushed upstairs, and found that the upper part of the house was on fire. Flames were everywhere. The little baby was lying fast asleep in her cot, unaware of the terrible danger.

I could see that the flames had entered her room, and that the curtains were on fire, and also some of the furniture was blazing. I rushed into the room, lifted the baby, and rolled it up in a blanket. I carried the baby in my arms, but the smoke and the flames were blinding me. I could not see where the door was. I crawled along the floor, holding the baby close to myself. I was able to get out of the door, but my hair and clothes were on fire. That is where I burned my hands. Fortunately, I was able to find the stairs, in spite of the dense smoke. I was able to take the baby down the stairs, and out to the safety of the street. I lay in hospital for a long time, before the skin on my hands healed over and grew better again. For more than a year, I had to wear special bandages like gloves. I suffered much pain for a long time afterward."

Mother looked at Fiona and said, "Can you guess, who that little baby was?" "Yes! It was you Fiona." Fiona realised what she had said about her mother's hands had been very cruel. Fiona began to cry, and then she stopped to think. "Mummy she said, I love your hair, and I love your face, and I love your eyes. Forgive my cruel words; Mummy, I love your hands most of all, because they were marked and scarred to save my life." Her mother smiled at Fiona, and said, "Of course, I'll forgive you!"

Now for a story from the New Testament. After Jesus had died, the Disciples met together in an upstairs room in Jerusalem for friendship. There were reports that Jesus had risen from the dead, and that he had been seen. One evening the disciples were together in the upper room, when Jesus appeared, and talked to them. Thomas was absent that evening. When he heard the report about Jesus being risen from the dead, he just did not believe it. Thomas was full of honest doubt. He said, that unless he could see the nailprints in the hands of Jesus, and the spear wound in his side, he would not believe the reports, that it really was Jesus.

A week past by,and one evening they were again in the upper room, and Thomas was there on that occasion. The doors had been locked. Suddenly, Jesus appeared in the room. He called for Thomas. "Look at the marks made by the nails in my hands, Thomas", he said. "Touch the spear-wound in my side. Happy are the people who believe, without having to see for proof". Thomas was no longer a doubter. He knew that Jesus had risen from the dead. He said to Jesus, "My Lord, and my God."

You have heard two stories about scarred hands today. People who care for other people sometimes get wounded or even killed by their enemies. If you love someone, then you are willing to take a risk to save them from danger. Christians believe, that when Jesus died on the cross, he showed the love of God for each one of us.

Prayer:

> Thank you Lord, for every one who cares for us.
> Help us to care for each other.
> We thank you for people whose hands
> are marked by honest work.
> Most of all we thank you,
> for the hands of Jesus,
> which were wounded for us.   Amen.

Hymn:

> Jesus' hands were kind hands, doing good to all. (JP. 134)

Teachers' Note: (1) Hands may be marked in many ways. We say that someone who was stealing "was caught red-handed." Hands may be marked by old age. Hands may be marked by honest work. Hands may be marked by our own carelessness. (Smoking). (2) Hands may be marked by our own sacrifice for others, as in the story. (3) Hands are very useful for doing good things (Pianist, Organist, Bricklayer, Nurse, Baker, Guitarist).

(b) The Praying Hands   *Week 8   Hands*

Some churches do not have a cross on the Communion Table, instead they have a pair of hands, held together in the praying position, and carved in wood. They represent an original painting of a pair of hands by a great artist named Albrecht Durer.

Albrecht was born the third child of a family which grew larger, until there were eighteen children. Because they were a very big family, Albrecht had to look after some of the younger children, when he became older. They lived in Nuremburg, a city in Germany. Their father was a Goldsmith. He dearly wanted the young Albrecht to become a goldsmith like himself. However Albrecht loved painting and drawing. So when he became a man he left home, and he met another man who also wanted to study to become an artist. So they rented a small cottage, as they had very little money.

Albrecht and his Painter-friend soon found that they could not earn enough to keep them both in food, clothing, and lodgings. So Albrecht's friend said to Albrecht, "Look I have found work in a restaurant. I will work and earn the money for us both to live on, and you can go to train as an Artist. You are younger than I am, and you are a far better Painter than I am. Go and learn to be a Wood-carver, and an Artist, and I will earn the wages to keep us both."

Albrecht's friend worked long hours washing dishes, and serving at the tables, and cleaning up after meals. Albrecht also worked as hard as he could to learn his craft. For many years, he sold his wood-carvings and his paintings, and saved a large sum of money. Albrecht said to his friend, "now we have enough money, you can go to learn to be an artist." His friend gave up his job in the restaurant, and began learning the art of painting pictures. However, he had worked so long with his hands in water, that they were no longer nimble. His hands had become sore, swollen, and stiff. He tried hard to be a painter, but Albrecht's friend realised that he could not succeed.

Albrecht resolved that he would always work to take care of his friend, because his friend had worked so long and hard for him. One day he arrived back to his house, and he saw his friend on his knees praying alone. He had his wrinkled hands clasped together in prayer. Albrecht thought to himself," I cannot make my friend's hands well again. Nevertheless, I will paint a picture of those worn hands as they are at this moment, for all the world to see how my friend worked for me". So he painted the picture, which everyone knows as, "The Praying Hands". The hands are beautiful in spite of their roughness through hard work. People love to have the picture, or to see a copy of the wood carving in church, because it helps them to think of praying to God.

Have you ever thought that people often use their hands to work for us. There was once a girl who applied for a job in a chocolate factory. She joined the queue with many others. Many of the girls ahead in the queue were given a job. When the girl's turn came to sit at the table with the personnel manager. He looked at her hands, and then told the girl that he could not give her a job.

She was very surprised, and asked why he would not employ her. The personnel manager said to her, "We do not employ people who bite their finger-nails. We are handling chocolates, which have to be kept free from any germs or infection. Everything has to be hygienic and clean. If an employee bites their finger-nails when they work here, then they might spread germs to the chocolates, which our customers have to eat. So we do not employ people who bite their nails." The girl went home, and made up her mind never to bite her finger-nails again.

People use their hands to serve us in so many ways. They must always be kept clean. Doctors and nurses in a hospital wash their hands many times every day, as they go from patient to patient. So hands may be worn rough with hard work or old age. As long as they are clean and useful hands, they are well pleasing to our friends and to God. Children can also lend a helping hand in the home or at school. The hands of the Lord Jesus were always kind hands.

Scouts and Guides often do good turns with their hands. They can do First Aid with bandages. They can tie many kinds of knots on a rope. They can dial 999 in an emergency. They can help Mum by carrying her bag or basket home from the shop. They can share their sweets or toffees with someone else. They can help to take the weeds out of their parents' garden. Can you think of other good deeds which children can do with their hands?

Prayer:

> O Lord, we thank you for the painting
> known as "Praying Hands.
> May it remind us, that we too,
> may use our hands in many good causes.
> Make our hands helpful and kind hands,
> that we may work not simply for ourselves,
> but for the good of others,
> and to your praise and glory.   Amen.

Hymn:

> Lord make me a mountain, standing tall for you. (JP. 421)

Teachers' Notes: (1) Hands may be worn and rough through hard work. Through old age, or by suffering such as Arthritis. (2) Hands must be kept clean because we touch food and can spread infections. (3) Above all, hands must be known as "kind hands". In the Bible "clean hands" signify "good behaviour," (see Psalm 24. verse 3.).

(c) **Beautiful Hands**

Week 8   Beautiful Hands

When John Wesley was alive, he spent most of his life riding about on horseback preaching to ordinary people. He had a little desk fitted to his saddle, so that he could rest a book upon it, and read as he made his way along the rough roads. He preached to many people about God's love for everyone, rich and poor. Many of the people he gathered around him were very poor indeed. Others were very rich. When he became older, he travelled about in a carriage, rather than on horseback.

Because he was away from his own home for long periods, he had to stay overnight in other peoples' houses. On one occasion, a very religious family invited him to have a meal with them and to stay overnight. The family gathered around the table, very honoured to have such a famous man in their home. At the meal, there was a young lady who had many rings on her fingers. The people knew that John Wesley preferred Methodists in those days not to wear expensive jewellery. Wesley wanted people to share their money with needy people, not to spend it on themselves.

One of the religious men at the meal had a very harsh attitude towards young people. He wanted John Wesley to rebuke the young lady. Suddenly, he took hold of the young lady by the wrist, and held up her hand before John Wesley. The religious man expected Wesley to condemn the young lady for wearing the rings on her fingers. However, John Wesley was a very kind man. He looked at the young lady, who was very embarrassed at being the centre of attention. Wesley gave her a kindly smile, and then he said, "What beautiful hands!"

The harsh man who expected the young lady to be condemned, was himself condemned, by Wesley for such a lack of good manners at the table. From this true story, we learn that we must not condemn other people, because we too might be failing in some other way, unknown to ourselves. What is important is that we treat each other kindly.

Let me tell you another story about hands. A young soldier lay very ill in hospital. He was very dejected and lonely. A Nurse thought it might help if the young soldier were to pray. He said that when he closed his eyes to pray, he could not remember the proper things for which to pray. So the Nurse told him to put his hands together, and she would show him how to pray in an ordered way.

The soldier held his hands together, as he was shown. The Nurse said, "Now you notice that your two thumbs are nearest you. This means that you always begin praying for those nearest yourself." So the soldier knew that he could pray for his family and friends.

Then the Nurse said, "The finger that comes next is your 'pointing finger'. That will remind you that you can pray for anyone who points out for us the way of life. For School-children this could include many people. The Teachers in school. The Minister in the Church. The Policeman who directs the traffic. The Lollipop lady/man who takes us over the road. The Scout or Guide Leader who shows us the way. The Sports or Music Teacher.

The Nurse pointed out that the next finger was the middle finger, the tallest of all. "This reminds us, she said, "to pray for the Leaders in our community. The Queen, the Prime Minister, the members of parliament,the Mayor and Mayoress, or any one else whom we consider to be high in authority.

Again, the Nurse pointed to the fourth finger. "This is the weakest finger of all. Ask anyone who is learning to play an musical instrument, such as the piano, or recorder. It is the fourth finger that is most difficult to control. It is our weakest finger. It is also the finger which wears the wedding ring" By this time the soldier understood, that he was to pray for the wounded soldiers; the sick people; old people; handicapped people.

Finally, the Nurse pointed to the smallest finger of all. "We should not forget to pray for small people and small things. Children, and the new baby, and also those little things that cause us inward worry". These two stories almost explain themselves. (1) We have learnt that hands are beautiful in themselves. (2) We have also learnt that hands can teach us how to order our prayers.

Prayer:

> Lord teach us all how to pray.
> Help us to pray for our friends.
> Help us to pray for those who guide us.
> Help us to pray for the leaders in our country.
> Help us to pray for anyone who is weak, or ill.
> Help us to pray for children like ourselves.   Amen.

Hymn:

> Spirit of God. (C&P.l. 63)

Teachers' Note: These stories need little further explanation.

(a) **Halloween and All Saints Day** *Week 9   Autumn Festivals*

"Halloween" is the old fashioned name for "Holy Evening." It is so named, because it is the evening before "All Saints Day." Children love Halloween, because it is the evening when they dress up in various costumes, and wear masks. Many children go to their friends and neighbours houses on this evening, collecting money from them, on the understanding of a "Trick or Treat." Halloween parties are fun! Games such as ducking for apples, or standing on a chair and dropping a fork on apples floating in a basin, are part of the celebrations.

Very few people believe in Witches nowadays. Hundreds of years ago, Halloween became associated with tales about the power of Witches. These so called Witches were said to have magical powers, and were supposed to be able to turn children into frogs. The common people were very fearful and superstitious in those days. Many an old lady was accused of being a Witch, and was put on a "Ducking Stool" and dipped up and down in the village pond. This was a very wicked thing to do in a Christian country, but sometimes even church members believed in witchcraft. In East Lancashire, in the area near Pendle Village, at Halloween, people still dress up as Witches, and ride on horses at the foot of Pendle Hill, to remind us of the old days.

Christian children do not believe that anyone could ever turn children into frogs. However, just as there are people in parts of Africa who still believe in Witch-Doctors, so people in England once believed that Witches could prepare magic potions that could make sick people better. Probably, many of these women were really people who had discovered that garden herbs, properly prepared, could could cure a tummy upset, or relieve a headache.

Halloween can be a lot of fun. It is held on the last day of October. It has a mystery about it, because All Saints Day follows it. A "Saint" is a holy person, so good, that the Church remembers them in a special way after they have died. Scotland honours as its Patron, St. Andrew. England honours St. George. Wales honours St. David. Ireland honours St. Patrick. All Saints day reminds us of "All Saints, known and unknown".

St. Martin of Tours is a very well known Saint. He lived in the fourth century. Both his parents were pagans. His father was an officer in the Italian army. Martin had to join the army when he was only fifteen years of age. He really did not like being a soldier. When his regiment was stationed in Amiens in Northern France something happened which made Martin world famous.

It was a very cold Winter's day. Every field was covered in white frost. Snow and sleet blew down the streets of Amiens. Martin was at the gate of the city, and he saw a poor beggar man, almost naked, trembling, and begging for money or food from the people passing by. No-one seemed to care for the poor beggar. The passers by just ignored him. Martin took off his warm cloak, and cut it in two with his sword. He gave half of it to the beggar man. He wrapped the other half around himself.

That night, Martin as he slept had a dream. He saw Jesus Christ, dressed in the half of cloak which he had given away. He heard Jesus say, "Martin has covered me with his cloak." The dream so affected Martin, that he soon was baptised as a Christian. He remained a soldier until he was twenty years old. Then he refused to accept his soldier's reward at the end of his term of service. Martin said to Julian Caesar, his Leader, "Hitherto I have served you as a soldier; let me now serve Christ." He became a person who preferred not to fight, giving up the army.

He formed a community of Hermits, which built the first monastery in Gaul. In the year 371 the people of Tours chose him for their Bishop. Other Bishops thought that he should not be a Bishop, because of his poor clothing and his untidy appearance. Martin, despite being the Bishop lived in a cell, and visited his Parish by foot, or riding on a donkey, or sailing in a small boat. Martin died on the 8th. November 397. The people remembered Martin by hanging up his half cloak, in a small church. The word "Chapel" comes from the Latin word "Cappella" which means "Cloak". The first "Chapel" was the little church, where they hung Martin's half-cloak.

Prayer:

> Father God, we thank you for all the good people,
> who lived long ago;
> people of every land, and race.
> Make us more like them,
> and more like Jesus Christ our Lord.   Amen.

Hymn:

> The Lord's Prayer. (C&P.l. 51)

Teachers Note: (1) Holy Evening and All Saints day have religious undertones. Christians believe that all children should attend some place of worship. (2) St. Martin was kind to poor people. He knew how to share his belongings. (3) A Chapel is as much God's house, as a large Cathedral.

(b) Guy Fawkes Day

It was the evening of Guy Fawkes day. The Children were gathered around their bonfire in Janine's back garden. Janine's father told the children the story behind this celebration. He said that it went back in English history, to the time when a famous soldier, called Guy Fawkes conspired to blow up the Houses of Parliament with gunpowder. He and his fellow conspirators meant to kill all the members of Parliament. They packed the cellar underneath with gunpowder. When the members were all sitting upstairs, the conspirators had secretly planned to set a match to the fuses, and destroy the building. Someone had a friend who was a member of Parliament. He did not want his friend to be killed, so he privately warned him by letter of the danger. As a result, the cellar was searched by soldiers, and Guy Fawkes and the conspirators were captured. The Parliament was saved, and everyone in it escaped with their lives. The children thanked Janine's Father for telling them the story.

The fire burned brightly, and the the trees and bushes in the garden could be seen quite clearly. Janine's mother brought out for the children, hot soup in small bowls, hamburgers, baked potatoes, hot dogs,, meat pies, and chocolate cake, and plenty of lemonade. In the group invited that evening, there were five boys and five girls. They were really enjoying themselves.

Then Janine's father brought out a box of fireworks. There were fizzbangs, Catherine wheels, traffic lights, and sky rockets. The children were warned by the adults that they must stand back from the fire, and that they must be careful never to pick up a firework that they thought had not gone off. One by one, Janine's father let off all the fireworks in his box. How excited and happy the children were.

In the darkness of the garden, no-one saw Billy pick up a firework which had not gone off. Billy slipped it into the pocket of his jacket, where no one could see it. Billy thought to himself that he could take this firework home, and let it off in the school yard next morning. He thought to himself, "No-one will ever know!" The children prepared to go home, and they thanked Janine and her parents for the delightful evening.

All at once, there was a loud bang from Billy's jacket pocket. The firework which Billy thought had gone out, still had been smouldering, unknown to him. Billy had his hand in his pocket at the time, and he was badly burned. He began to cry out in pain. Janine's father quickly pulled off Billy's jacket. Janine's mother looked at the boy's burned hand, and immediately 'phoned 999, and called the ambulance. Billy was quickly rushed to hospital, crying all the way, because of the pain in his burnt hand. The other children felt that Billy had spoiled the evening for all of them. He had been disobedient, but they were still very worried about Billy.

Both Billy's parents and Janine's parents went up by car to the Hospital to see the disobedient boy. The nurses had bandaged Billy's hand. The doctor said to the adults, "I think that Billy should stay in hospital all night. He is suffering from shock. We'll see how he is in the morning." So Billy lay in the hospital bed, and was very frightened that night.

Next day, the doctor allowed Billy to go home with his parents. Billy's mother said to him, "Billy, now you know that disobedience brings its own reward." Billy went round to Janine's father and mother, and said that he was sorry for being disobedient, and for putting the firework in his pocket, after being warned.

Billy hand was very painful for about a week or more. Eventually the burn healed over and became better. However, the burn left a scar on Billy's hand, and every time Billy looked at the scar, he made up his mind that he would never be disobedient again.

Prayer:

Lord, may we appreciate the kindness of other people.
Lord, help us to listen to the good advice,
of our parents, and our teachers.
Help us not to be disobedient.
Make us thankful for Doctors and Nurses,

and everyone who cares for us.

Make us very careful on Bonfire evening.   Amen.

Hymn:

Light up the fire. (C&P.l. 55)

Teachers' Note: (1) To be invited to someone else's home, is a privilege. We ought to show appreciation for kindness shown to us. (2) Being disobedient can hurt us, because usually there is a good reason for rules. (3) Billy was very brave to go back and apologise for his disobedience.

(c) Remembrance Day   *Week 9   Autumn Festivals*

At the eleventh hour, of the eleventh day, of the eleventh month of the year, we celebrate "Remembrance Day." The Poppy is known as "The flower of Remembrance," and we wear it to remind us of the many sailors, soldiers, marines, and airmen, who died in war.

Colonel John McCrae lived before the First World war. In his younger years, he had served as a gunner in the South African War. Later, he studied to become a Doctor. Because of his skill, he became a Professor of Medicine at McGill University in Montreal, in Canada. When the First World War broke out, John McCrea volunteered for the army. The Authorities decided that he would be more useful as a Doctor, so he landed in France as a Medical Officer in the Canadian Army.

He served with the soldiers on the battlefield, tending their wounds. At the second battle of Ypres in the year 1915, he was in charge of a small First-aid post. It was here, during a quite hour, that he wrote in pencil his famous poem, "In Flanders Fields." In the poem, he mentions that there were poppies growing between the crosses which marked out the soldiers graves. Someone sent the poem to the, "Punch" magazine, where it was published. Since that time the poem has been read all over the world.

Sad to say, three years later, Colonel John McCrae was brought gravely ill, to a large hospital on the Northern coast of France. After being in hospital for three days, he was allowed to be brought to the balcony of the Hospital. There he could look over the waves of the English Channel, and see the white cliffs of Dover in England. That same night, Colonel John McCrae died. If you ever go to France on holiday, you may visit his grave in a cemetery at Wimereux. On a clear day, you may also see the white cliffs of Dover across the water in England.

Miss. Moina Michael, an American lady read John McCrae's poem, and she also wrote a poem about the poppies on the graves of the soldiers. She called her poem "The Victory Emblem." At the time, she worked for the Young Men's Christian Association, which was very interested in helping Ex-service men.

Two days before the the First Great War ended, on the 8th. November 1918, some of the Y.M.C.A overseas War Secretaries were holding a meeting at her house. The Secretaries presented her with a gift of money. Miss. Michael went out and bought twenty five red poppies with the money, and then she sold them to each one of the Secretaries present. This group of ladies were the first group of poppy buyers and sellers in the world.

One of the Secretaries, a French lady, Madame Guerin, travelled the world, encouraging people to make artificial poppies, to sell to help ex-service men and their dependents. The Field Marshal, Earl Haig, became the Founder-President of "The British Legion." The first Poppy day in Britain was held on November the eleventh, 1921. The original manufactured poppies were made in France, and it was these which were sold on the first Poppy Day. The poppies, wreathes, and Remembrance Crosses, which we use nowadays are all made in a modern factory in Richmond, Surrey.

Yet another way of remembering is to set up a landmark of some kind. In most towns and villages there is a war memorial situated in a prominent place. It is often called a "Cenotaph", which means an "empty tomb." Soldiers, sailors, marines, and airmen who were killed in past wars may have a grave in some faraway place, but once every year, their friends remember them by meeting at a local Cenotaph. If you look closely at a war memorial, very often the words inscribed on it are, "Lest we forget." This is another way of saying, "We remember you!" If you look again, you will see that on it there are many names of ex-service men and women from your district, who were killed in war. These names are carved in the stone.

We keep the eleventh hour, of the eleventh day, of the eleventh month, (November) as a special time, because the First World War (1914-1918), ceased at that time, and a peace agreement was signed. Older people call it "Armistice Day." Ex-service men and women, march to a church Parade Service, held on the Sunday nearest to the 11th. November.

People wear poppies at this time, because the poppies were the wild flower that the soldiers of the First World War saw growing around them in Flanders battlefield. Although the poppies were often cut down by shells and bombs, they always grew up again the following year. So the poppy became a symbol of "Hope", and "Sacrifice for others." When you buy a manufactured poppy, the money which you pay for your poppy, will go to the Royal British Legion to help needy ex-service people, and those members of their families who depend upon them.

Prayer:

> Father, God, we thank you for those brave people,
> of the Navy, Army, and Air-force,
> who laid down their lives for their country.
> We pray that all wars may cease,
> and that all the world may learn
> to live together in peace.   Amen.

Hymn:

> Make me a channel of your peace. (The Prayer of St. Francis.)
> (C&P.2. 147)

Teachers' Note: (1) "Remembrance Day" is kept in every country throughout the world. People of every nation have been killed in fighting wars. There will be many sad hearts everywhere on this day. (2) It is always better to live in peace with each other, because war is a waste of human life. (3) We must not glorify war, yet we must never forget that other brave people have died to defend our freedom.

(a) Useful Books

Week 10   Useful Things

Have you ever thought about the importance of books? When you were born, your name was reported to the District Registrar of births, deaths and marriages. When you are older, you may need a "birth certificate" to prove your age. The Registrar will write out a certificate for you, from the information in his book. This book is kept in a fire-proof safe, so that it cannot be destroyed. If you were baptised as a baby, again, your name was written down in the Church Baptism Register. Your teacher keeps a Class Register of all your names, and marks it everyday you attend school.

Books are very important in life. Can you remember the first book you were taught to read at school. Long ago, when your Grandad and Grandma were taught to read at their old schools, the pages of words all had a similar kind of rhyming sound. Imagine your Grandad and Grandma as little children. This is what a page of their reading book might sound like. It will sound funny to you!

Pat had a hat,
and Pat had a bat.
Pat had a cat.
Pat saw a rat.
The cat sat on the mat,
and the rat sat on the hat.
Pat was fat.
The cat was fat.
The rat was fat.
Pat and the cat and the rat,
All sat on the mat,
The mat was flat.
And that was that!
What about the bat?

When we learn to read, all the books in our language are available to us. There are very special books in all religions. The Koran for Muslims, for example. Hindus and Sikhs also have holy books. The Bible is the worlds best selling book yet some people only pretend to read it.

Old Mr. and Mrs. Bluffer had a large family Bible in their cupboard. Really, they never read it. One afternoon there was a knock at the door. The Minister was outside. He was making a visit. Mr. and Mrs. Bluffer looked out from behind the curtains and saw him. They did not open the door immediately, but instead they tidied up their fireplace. They rushed about, putting the newspapers under the cushions on the settee. They took the big family Bible out of the cupboard and dusted it, and put it on the table; just as if they had been reading it.

The Minister knocked the door a second time. This time, Mr. and Mrs. Bluffer opened the door. "O what a surprise to see you!", they said. "Do come in." The Minister came in and they talked together. Mr. and Mrs. Bluffer were rather poor. The Minister wanted to help them. He asked them if they read the Bible, and what was their favourite chapter. Mr. and Mrs. Bluffer, told a lie, and said, "We read the Bible every day, and our favourite chapter is Psalm 23."

As the two old people fussed about preparing tea in the back kitchen, the Minister opened the family Bible at Psalm 23. He put a new ten pound note in between the page and closed the Bible. Mr. and Mrs. Bluffer drank a cup of tea with the Minister. Then he went home. They took the family Bible off the table, and put it back into the cupboard.

A year passed, and the Minister made another visit. Again they looked out of the window. The same thing occurred. Mr. and Mrs. Bluffer took the family Bible out of the cupboard, dusted it, and tidied up the settee. The Minister knocked the door a second time. Again, Mr. and Mrs. Bluffer pretended that they had not known it was the Minister. Again, they made tea for him in the back kitchen.

The Minister wanted to help the poor couple again, so he quietly opened the Bible at Psalm 23. The new ten pound note was still lying between the pages, where he had put it the year before. The Minister now knew that this old couple never read their Bible after all. He knew that they had told him a lie. So, the Minister quietly removed the new ten pound note from the Bible. After the visit, Mr. and Mrs. Bluffer put the family Bible away to gather dust in the cupboard again. They never realised what they had lost because they never read their Bible!

Now no-one is saying that you will find a new ten pound note each time you open your Bible! We are saying that you might read something more valuable to you than finding a ten pound note. Do you think the Minister was right to have taken back a gift, he had already given?

Prayer:

> We thank you for the Holy Bible.
> We thank you for all good and Holy Books.
> Help us not to pretend to read them,
> but rather to read, meditate, learn,
> and inwardly digest all that we read.   Amen.

Hymn:

> The best book to read is the Bible. (JP. 234)

Teachers' Note: (1) Books are our good friends. We must treat them with great care. (2) The Bible is a book full of stories worth reading. (3) We need to ask God to help us to understand what we read.

(b) Useful Bells

Week 10   Useful Things

Did you know that the word "Bell" comes from the word "Bellow?" A bull makes a bellow noise when it snorts. When we come nearer Christmas time, often we sing about Bells. It may be about about Jingle bells, or sleigh bells, or church bells.

Does anyone know the names of three flowers which are bells? The answer is, "Bluebells, Harebells, and Canterbury bells."

Let us think of a number of useful bells which affect our lives.

(i)   *The Morning Bell*

This is the bell which we do not always like to hear in our ears. Some of us have an alarm clock at home. Some of us have a radio alarm which wakes us up. Some people are awakened by the telephone telling them the time. These bells tell us "Wake up sleepy head. Arise and shine; it is time to get up! "

(ii)   *The Learning Bell*

Years ago, every school had a bell. The Headteacher rang it the first time to warn his pupils that in five minutes, everyone had to line-up, and be ready for the second bell. When the second bell rang, all the children marched into school. When this bell rings it means "Come and learn!"

(iii)   *The Door Bell*

It is good when a house has a door bell. When someone calls at the door, then all the caller has to do is to press the bell. When this bell rings it says "Open the door, please".

(iv)   *The Telephone Bell*

The Telephone bell rings very often. It says "Someone wants to speak to you" .

(v)   *The Fire Alarm Bell*

This is the bell which we do not like to hear. Yet, it rings out a very useful warning, "Be cool; Be calm: Be collected: Get outside quietly and quickly."

(v)   *The Church Bells*

Outside the town of Nelson, at Southfield, in Lancashire,there is a little Methodist Church, right in the middle of a farm yard. Two Hundred years ago, the owner of the farm built this little church as part of his farm buildings. He used to provide a room, a bed, and food for the Reverend John Wesley, when he was passing through on horseback. There is a single bell on a rope outside. Today, the visiting Minister or Preacher is allowed to toll the bell, and call the people to church. If the preacher is late, some of the children may pull the bell rope instead. Many Anglican and Catholic churches have bells. They have specially trained people to ring them. The bell-ringers are called "Campanologists".

(vi)   *The Leper's Bell*

Long ago in England, there were people who had contracted the disease known as "Leprosy". It was a skin disease, that wasted away, fingers, and toes, and the skin of the body. To prevent the disease spreading among people, the lepers were forced to leave their own homes, and live outside the towns and villages. Very often they lived together in tents or caves. They were very poor and sick, and no-one wanted to speak to them. They sometimes carried a bell, and when anyone drew near them, they would ring their bell, and shout out, "Unclean, Unclean! Passers-by would know to keep away from the leper. Some churches had a narrow window in the back wall or the side wall. These windows were known as "Lepers windows". The poor sick people were not allowed ever to attend church. Instead, they crouched outside, and looked in at the church service. If anyone approached them, they rang their bell.

There is a story in the Bible about ten men who were lepers. There is no mention of a bell in the story. It is a very interesting story, because it was written in St Luke's Gospel. Now St Luke was a Doctor, so we have a Doctor's account of the power of Jesus.

Jesus was going on a journey to Jerusalem. He passed down a road that went between Samaria and Galilee. As he went, he came to a village where he met ten men. They were lepers. These ten men lived outside the village, because people regarded them as unclean. Lepers would often come and live together to help each other. Some of the lepers came from Samaria and some were Jews. These ten lepers were both outcasts and beggars.

When Jesus appeared they all shouted together, "Jesus, Master, have pity on us." Jesus did not touch them on this occasion, but rather told them to go and show themselves to the Priest and they would be well. This instruction was because the old law of Moses commanded that such people should show themselves to the Priest for a medical check-up before going back among healthy people. As they went, the miracle occurred. They were made better.

One of the ten men realising that he was now well, returned to Jesus. The man, now cured from his leprosy, knelt down before Jesus, and thanked him. Jesus said, "Did I not cleanse ten lepers, where are the other nine. Rise up, your faith has made you healthy." Hearing this story again, it does seem sad that none of the other nine lepers who were cured ever came back to say, "thank you" to Jesus.

Prayer:

> Lord teach us all to be thankful,
> for health and for strength;
> for homes and for our friends.
> We thank you for schools and Teachers.
> Help us to take care of our bodies,
> and to do nothing to spoil our environment.   Amen.

Hymn:

> The bell of creation. (C&P.2. 86)

Teachers' Note: (1) Bells make a noise, but the noise is usually a helpful noise; a primitive means of communication. (2) Children need to be encouraged by being told that leprosy now can be cured. (3) It is always good to thank people who have been kind to us. If they are far away, we can write a letter.

(c) Useful Jars and Trumpets

Sometime objects which are made for one use, end up by being used for another. Have you ever seen a working man's old boot with beautiful flowers in it, hanging up on a garden wall? It makes a lovely decoration. Have you ever seen old car tyres tied around the prow of a fishing boat, to prevent damage to the hull when the boat scrapes against the harbour wall. The idea works very well! Have you ever seen a railway goods van being used on a farm as a hen house? The hens are cozy and warm inside it. Have you ever seen an old disused bath in the middle of a field. Farmers use them as a drinking troughs for the cows and other animals. Our talk today is about how Gideon found another use for clay jars and trumpets. Gideon was one of the famous leaders sent to lead the Israelites, some years after the death of Joshua. The Israelites who had come out of Egypt, had reached the Promised Land of Canaan. They set up their houses, and planted vineyards, established farms, and they raised donkeys, sheep and cattle. Sometimes the Midianites, who were a large tribe of desert raiders, used to come as an army, riding camels in great numbers. They would steal the cattle, donkeys, and sheep from the Israelite farmers, and use up their corn and wheat.

The Israelite people prayed to God for help. God sent a messenger to Gideon, who said, "I am sending you, Gideon, to save Israel from the Midianites". Gideon wanted to be sure that he was God's choice of a Leader. So he said to God, "Tomorrow morning, I am going to put a sheep's fleece, (woollen coat) on the ground. If there is dew on the woollen fleece, but not on the ground, then I will know that you, Lord, are going to choose me as your Leader for the people." Early next morning, Gideon was able to wring a bowlful of water from the woollen fleece, yet the ground was dry.

Gideon was not completely satisfied, so he asked God for one further proof that he was the right man as Leader. The second request was that he would put the woollen fleece out again, and that next morning the fleece would be dry, but the ground would be wet. God gave Gideon the proof he needed. Next morning, the fleece was dry, but the ground was wet. So Gideon was sure that he was God's choice as Leader of the people.

Gideon called all the tribes of Israel together to go to war against the Midianites. He and his army were encamped across the valley from the Midianite army camp. God told Gideon that he had too many soldiers. Gideon reduced the size of his army by telling the soldiers that anyone who felt afraid could go home. Twenty-two thousand soldiers went home. Ten thousand soldiers remained.

God told Gideon, "There are still too many soldiers." Take your men down to the river to quench their thirst. You may separate the soldiers into two groups. Those who scoop up water in their hand, and lap like a dog, must be separated from those who kneel down at the river to drink." Those who lapped from their hands were more alert to the enemy, and they avoided the leeches in the water. Only three hundred, out of the ten thousand acted in the right manner. Gideon sent all the others home.

When it became dark, Gideon attacked the Midianite camp, when their soldiers were asleep in their tents. Gideon's plan was that each of his three hundred Israelite soldiers should carry a trumpet, and a burning oil torch hidden inside an earthenware jar.

They surrounded the Midianite camp in the darkness of the night. Then they made a loud noise, each soldier shouting at the top of his voice, "A sword for the Lord and for Gideon." They blew their trumpets in the pitch darkness, and broke their jars, making more noise, and the burning oil torches blazed from all sides in the darkness. The Midianite soldiers were frightened out of their wits, and ran out of their tents, and began to fight one with the other. Their whole army became so terrified that they all ran away. Gideon and his men attacked them in the darkness and defeated them. There was peace in the land for the next forty years.

Prayer:

> Hear us good Lord,
> and help us to defeat all that is evil,
> by doing what is good, pure, and right.
> Teach us that God wants us to live in peace.
> Show us that we all have individual gifts,
> and talents that we may use to God's glory,
> and to the service of our community.   Amen.

Hymn:

> Peace perfect peace. (C&P.l 53)

Teachers' Note: (Judges Ch.6.v. 36-40 to Ch.7. 21). (1) Gideon separated careless soldiers, and sent them away, from the three hundred soldiers who were always on their guard, even when drinking from a river. We all need to be observant. (2) Gideon used trumpets, and burning torches to frighten the enemy at night. The Midianites were bullies over the Israelite farmers. Bullies are often cowards at heart. (3) Gideon's victory brought peace for forty years. God wants all lands and people to enjoy peace. Even children can make peace.

(a) The Boy with the Kind Heart   *Week 11   Emergencies*

Hasan was born in Birmingham. His parents originally came from India. They came over to England to work in one of the car factories. Hasan was one of those boys who always acted as though he was kind-hearted. He seemed to know just what to do when there was an emergency. When he left school, he became assistant to the local milk-man who drove the milk van. This particular milk-man delivered milk to shops during the day.

One day, as he walked along the road to work, he heard a woman screaming at the top of her voice. "Someone help me." Hasan ran to the house. The woman was standing at the top of the stairs, waving her arms. A big black cat was jumping about all over the place. Hasan popped his head in the door and asked whether he could help in any way. The woman told him that she had just emptied a large size tin of salmon on to a plate, and turned her back to go into the kitchen, when the cat had jumped up on the table, and knocked the tin on to the floor. After eating the remains of the salmon, the cat had somehow managed to stick it's head inside the tin. No matter how much the cat tried, the tin would not come off. The cat became frantic with fear, and was running up and down, and round and round. The woman was frightened, and did not know what to do.

Hasan immediately ran up the stairs, but the cat fell down the stairs, unable to see because of the tin over its head. The woman began to scream again! Hasan eventually caught the cat, and very quietly stroked it, to calm it down. Then he gently pulled the salmon tin off the cat's head. Smiling, Hasan gave the woman back her black cat. She thanked him, and said that he was a hero. Hasan did not feel like a hero as he off went to his job, with the milkman delivering crates of bottles of milk.

Hasan, greeted his driver, Joe, and climbed into to cab beside the driver's seat. Off they went, down the Coventry Road, stopping here and there at shops to deliver crates of milk. It was a beautiful sunny day, and a woman pushing her baby in a pram, stopped at a shop. She went inside the shop, but forgot to put on the brake.

The street was on a hill. When the woman was inside the shop, the wind blew the pram, and it began to move slowly at first, and then faster, travelling along the pavement with increasing speed. People realised that the pram had turned slightly, and was heading towards the busy road. It was heading for two lanes of moving lorries and cars. Everyone began to shout, but no-one did anything.

Just at that very moment, the milk-van came down the road. Hasan heard the people shouting, and he looked out of the cab window to see the speeding pram very near the edge of the pavement. He shouted to Joe, his driver, to come close to the pavement. Hasan opened the milk-van door, and hung out, with one arm stretched out. As the milk-van came close alongside the moving pram, Hasan caught hold of the pram handle. He held on to it with all his might. As the milk-van slowed down, so the pram slowed down. Soon it had come to a halt. The baby's mother in the shop, hearing the screeching of brakes, and the crowd shouting, ran out to the street to find her baby and pram had gone.

Then she saw the crowd gathered around Hasan. The mother ran to get her baby in the pram, for no-one knew who owned it. Tears were coming down her cheeks, as she thanked Hasan for rescuing her little one from what might have been a terrible accident.

Hasan, was embarrassed by all the fuss. He said,"I only did my duty." He gave them all a big grin, and standing on the milk-van , he shouted to the crowd, "Be Prepared." As he said this, he gave the Scout salute, and the milk-van moved away. No one ever knew whether Hasan really was a Scout, or whether he was only having fun!.

The important point in this story, is that Hasan liked helping people. He could have minded his own business, and not been any help to anyone. He was old enough to know his own mind. I am sure that his parents must have been proud of him!

Prayer:

> Lord, some of us have eyes that do not see.
> We have ears that do not hear.
> Open our eyes, and open our ears,
> that when opportunity calls us to help someone,
> may we not hesitate to show that we have kind hearts.
> Keep us prepared to be active in doing good.   Amen.

Hymn:

> Cross over the road. (C&P.1. 70).

Teachers' Note: (1) Hasan did not need to look for an opportunity to help, he was prepared. The emergencies just happened in everyday life. (2) Hasan had a very generous nature. You can give other things beside money. We may give praise, thanks, friendship, or encouragement. (3) Hasan had a saving sense of humour. Can you see the funny side of things? A smile goes a very long way!

(b) The Telephone Emergency   *Week 11   Emergencies*

It is never wise to climb a mountain alone. It is better to have one companion, at least. David lived in Belfast, and he would have liked to be a mountain climber, but he had no training or experience. He was sixteen years of age and had left school. He often walked alone across the Cave Hill, which overlooked the city of Belfast. From the top of the Cave Hill on a clear day, the Isle of Man may be seen, lying far out in the Irish Sea. You may look South and see the Mountains of

Mourne. Most people like to look down on the city of Belfast, where far below, the houses, buses cars, and ships look like little toys.

There is a sheer rock face on the hill, which is named "McCart's Fort." Most people know it is "Napoleon's Nose", because the Hill is shaped like Napoleon Bonaparte's face. On the cliff side there are four caves going into the rock. David had always wanted to climb the cliff and to enter all the caves.

On a sunny day, he climbed very easily into the first cave, because it was the lowest, and the largest of the four. Away in past history, the first cave had been used by smugglers. Nowadays, anyone may walk into it and explore. From that point, David climbed upwards to the second cave, and then to the third. He was very near the fourth cave, high up on the cliff face, when he slipped on wet clay, and fell all the way down. to the stone path below. As he fell, he gave a loud scream, before he hit the ground. He lay there moaning, and unconscious, with blood on his head and face.

There were no adults about, but five children were gathering Bilberries at the foot of the cliff. The children ran to where David the injured climber was lying on the ground. What could they do? They just looked at each other. Then one of them said, "Let us run down to the Belfast Castle, and use the telephone to call the ambulance." Two of the children remained beside the injured climber. The others ran down the hill, through the forest, about a mile distant.

When they reached the telephone box, they dialled 999. A voice enquired, "Which service do you require?" They all said down the telephone at once, "Ambulance". However, they could not give any address to the Operator. Instead they explained that the accident had occurred at the foot of the cliff. "Please, do not move from the 'phone box, until the ambulance arrives," the operator said. So the children waited. Soon, they could hear the whine of the ambulance siren as it made its way up the long Castle Drive-way. They were trembling with excitement.

The ambulance men hurried out of the ambulance, and followed the children back through the forest, and up the cliff path. Both men were carrying a stretcher between them. When they reached David, the climber, he was lying unconscious on the path. The ambulance men carefully tied David on the stretcher, with what looked like bandages. Then they carried him down the mountain-side to the waiting ambulance. The children followed in silence. The men put David inside the waiting ambulance, and rushed him off to the hospital.

Just before the ambulance started off, the Driver put his head out of the ambulance, and said, " Well done children. Thank You!." The children went off home to tell their parents about their adventure on the Cave Hill. On the following day , they read in the evening newspaper, that a climber by the name of "David" had fallen down the cliff. He had suffered a fractured skull, and broken ribs. The newspaper reported that David was recovering in the City Hospital. The children talked together, and they decided that it would be very useful to learn about, "First Aid" in case anything like this should ever happen again. Most of them later had "First Aid" training in youth organisations, after they reached the age of twelve.

Prayer:

> Father God, we thank you for your almighty care,
> over all your family, old and young alike.
> Help us in any emergency, to remain calm.
> Bless ambulance workers, nurses, and doctors.
> Bless those good people who have learnt "First Aid."
> Make us wise, so that we may not be foolish,
> and cause accidents by our behaviour.   Amen.

Hymn:

> For the beauty of the earth. (C&P.l. 11)

Teachers' Note: (1) A genuine accident can happen when we least expect it. (2) Sometime people cause emergencies by their own foolish actions. (3) In an emergency the Police, the Fire Services, and the Ambulance Service are there to help us quickly.

(c) The Man who Stood the Storm   *Week 11   Emergencies*

Paul had been arrested in the seaside town of Caesarea, by the Roman soldiers. The people had complained about him preaching about Jesus. Because Paul was a Roman Citizen, he had the right to be tried in a Roman Court at Rome. So he was taken with other prisoners to a Roman ship. The ship set sail to go from Caesarea to Italy. They were sailing across the Mediterranean Sea. The sailing ship took rather a long time because the winds were blowing in the wrong direction. They had to take a zig-zag course, to try to catch the wind in their sails.

Then a North-Eastern hurricane began to blow, and it raged for a long time. The sailing boat was thrown off its course. The seamen were forced to throw the cargo overboard into the sea in order to to make the ship lighter. Paul said to the seamen, "You should have taken my advice, and remained in the harbour at the island of Crete." However, the storm continued to blow for fourteen days longer.

Paul told the seamen, that the previous night he had a dream. In this dream, the Angel of the Lord had told him that the ship would be wrecked, but that the crew, soldiers and prisoners would be saved from drowning. Everyone on board had not been eating enough food, because of the storm. Paul advised them all to have one good meal. So the 276 men on board the ship had a good meal. By this time they had lightened the ship, throwing into the sea, the rest of the sacks of grain, which had been used for making bread.

In the morning light, they looked towards the shore, and they saw a bay with a sandy beach. So they cut the anchors, hoisted the sails, and made for the beach. The ship struck a sand-bank, and the heavy waves beat upon the ship, and broke it to pieces. Everyone held on to broken planks of wood, and were washed up the beach. They found out afterwards that the place was the island of Malta.

Because they were wet through, they set out to gather brushwood to make a big fire. Just as Paul was putting the firewood on the fire, a snake among the brushwood bit him on the hand, and held on to his hand. Paul put his hand over the fire, and the snake fell off into the flames. Everyone waited to see if Paul would die from the poison in the snake-bite. Paul just carried on as usual, and the bite caused him no harm. After three months they found another boat. They set sail and later arrived at the city of Rome.

Paul was put into prison, and later condemned to death at Rome. This story tells us about the dangers and difficulties of being a Christian during the days of the Roman Empire. Most of the early Christians at Rome were slaves. Later, the Roman Emperor, Constantine, became a Christian, and rich and powerful people also became Christians. Rome became a Christian city. All persecution of Christians stopped. This was due to the faithfulness of earlier Christians such as Paul.

Prayer:

> We pray for all who sail the seas in ships.
> We pray that they may pass through the storms,
> and arrive safe home to harbour again.
> We pray for the families of seamen.
> Make us thankful for the food that comes to us
> from abroad.   Amen.

Hymn:

> Spirit of God. (C&P.l. 63)

Teachers' Notes: (1) The apostle Paul travelled around establishing new churches. (2) He was a brave man and understood the sailing of ships in bad weather. (By trade he was a tent maker and a sail maker) (3) He kept himself strong in his faith by praying to God, and helping people.

(a) Childrens' Christmas   *Week 12   Looking Towards Christmas*

Soon it will be Christmas! Let us take the word "Christmas" which has nine letters, and see what each letter immediately suggests to us. Children will be able to supply other words.

C is the easiest letter. It could mean carols, crib, candles, crackers, cakes, or cards. For shop-keepers it could mean cash! Most of all we must not forget "Christ."

H is more difficult. It could refer to Holly, hymns, or the happiness which Christmas brings.

R is easier. It could refer to Reindeers, rejoicing, or the Robin on the Christmas cards.

I is difficult. It could refer to the Infant Jesus, or to the Ivy beside the Holly.

S reminds us of the star, the Shepherds in the Bible story, Santa, his sleigh, the snow, stockings, or just shops!

T reminds us of toys, trees, tinsel, trimmings, it might remind you of the Turkey many people eat.

M reminds us of Mary, who was the mother of the baby Jesus. It suggests the manger. Christmas is always a merry time, when we eat mince-pies.

A reminds us of the Angels who sang at Advent, of the birth. They made the "Annunciation." We must not forget the animals in the stable.

S appears a second time in the word "Christmas." . The Bible says, that when the baby was born in the "Stable" he was to be called "Jesus" because he was to be a "Saviour".

Fifty years ago, three little boys were looking towards Christmas. One was aged seven, one aged five, and one aged four. Their mother had just died in hospital, after a serious illness lasting two years. Then their father fell very ill, and he too had to go into hospital. A kind Aunt took the boys into her little house for a short time. Of course, they could not stay there for long. There was not much room for everybody. The question was, "Who would care for them?"

The representative from Dr. Barnardo's Children's Home called to see them. He offered the three little boys a home with the other orphan children in the big house, with the, "Ever open door." Dr. Barnardo's Home always had the front door open, with a second door in the hall locked to keep out the cold, and intruders. A light burned above the doorway all night long. A sign outside read, "No destitute child ever refused admission." Another notice said, "Please press the bell."

The three little boys joined the biggest family they had ever seen. There were many other children being cared for by these very kind people. It was nearly

Christmas time, and the Staff and the children were busy making Christmas decorations to hang up in every room. These, they made by twisting coloured crepe paper mixed with tinsel, and hanging it down the walls. Everyone seemed so happy. Smiling, they welcomed the three newcomers.

When Christmas Eve came round, the three little boys went to bed in their dormitory, with all the other children. Next morning, they awoke and at the bottom of every child's bed, there was a sackful of toys of every kind. All the children were happy that morning, even though many of them had no parents.

Through-out the previous week, they had been invited out to Christmas parties. However, on Christmas day, there was the biggest feast of all! The children and Staff sat round a large table for their Christmas dinner. Everyone wore paper hats, and pulled crackers. Each girl and boy was very happy, because they knew that they were celebrating the Birthday of Jesus. A lady that evening read them a short account of the very first Christmas.

Six months passed by, and the father of the three little boys became well again. He was discharged from hospital. One day he called at Dr. Barnardo's Home. He thanked the Staff at the Home for their care for his family. He collected his three boys to take them home again. The boys felt a little sorry to have to say, "Good Bye" to all their new-found friends, and the Staff who had been so kind to them. They looked forward to being in their own house again with their father. They were thankful that kind people had made Christmas such a happy time for them.

Prayer:

We thank you, O Lord, for sending Jesus to our world.
We remember that He was born in a stable.
We thank you for our homes, and the food we eat.
We pray for poor children at Christmas time.
Bless them, and bless all those kind people
who take care of them.
Bless and bring healing to children in hospital.   Amen.

Hymn:

Come and join the celebration. (JP. 323)

Teachers' Note: (1) Christmas is a time of rejoicing about the birth of Jesus. We must never take the Christ out of Christmas. (2) It is also a time for receiving and giving presents and festivity, because God's gift to us was Jesus. (3) The deeper meaning of Christmas makes us all feel uncomfortable, because it has to do with caring for the poor and homeless.

(b) Old People at Christmas Time   *Week 12 Looking Toward Christmas*

Everyone agrees that Christmas is a wonderful time for children. Have you ever thought about old people at Christmas time? Simeon lived in the large city of Jerusalem. He was a very old man when Jesus was born. God had promised Simeon that he would not die until he had seen the Messiah. Simeon had waited a life-time, and nothing had happened. Eight days after Mary had her baby, she and her husband, Joseph, took the Jesus up to the Temple which is in the city of Jerusalem. They came to dedicate him to the Lord.

Simeon was there, at the time when Mary and Joseph brought the baby into the Temple. Simeon took the baby in his arms. He thanked God that he had lived long enough to see the baby Saviour. Simeon said, "Now I can die in peace, for I have seen the Saviour with my own eyes."

There was another old lady in the Temple by the name of Anna. She was eighty-four years of age. She had been married for only seven years, before her husband had died. After that she had lived as a widow alone, for many years. People spoke of her as a "Prophetess". Anna never left the Temple. She spent much of her time fasting and praying. She met Mary and Joseph when they were visiting Jerusalem. She saw and admired the new baby Jesus. Anna after saying a prayer of thanksgiving, went out to tell people that the Messiah had been born.

Nowadays, not every old person looks forward to Christmas. A hundred years ago, Charles Dickens wrote a story called, "A Christmas Carol" about an old man by the name of Ebenezer Scrooge, who did not like Christmas. There are other reasons why some old people do not like Christmas time. For them it may be a sad time. It brings back memories of events that happened long ago.

The children at the village school used to wonder why old Grannie Gray did not like Christmas time. She lived in a little cottage down the School Lane. She never put up decorations in her house. She never sent Christmas cards. She never prepared a special Christmas dinner. She never went to the Church Candle-light service. She was happy when Christmas was past. One peculiar thing, however, she did do. She always put a wreath of holly on her front door.

One evening in late December, the children at the village school decided to go Carol singing around the houses. They could not very well pass Grannie Gray's lovely little cottage. So they stopped outside the front door, with the holly wreath on it, and began to sing, "The First Noel." Grannie Gray opened the front door, and looked out into the darkness. She saw the children. To their surprise she invited them inside, to sing another Carol.

As the children sang a second Carol, they noticed that there were two framed photographs on the sideboard. Around them was a small piece of holly. The photographs were of two young soldiers in their uniform. When the children finished singing, one of them said to Grannie Gray, "Grannie, tell us why you do not like Christmas?"

A little tear came into her eye as she spoke. She said, "My husband died very early in our marriage, but we had two fine boys in our family. At the outbreak of war, they both joined the British Army. Away back in the year 1944, I had news that both of my sons had been killed in the war. The Post Office boy who brought the telegram with the sad news in it, came two days before Christmas. He rode a bicycle. When he handed to me the Telegram inside a yellow envelope, he never knew that he had brought bad news. Every year, I put a holly wreath on my front door, and I keep a sprig of holly behind these two photographs of my two sons. Really, Christmas is a time of sad memories for me."

The children Carol singers were very silent for a moment or two. Then one of them said, "Granny Gray we were very sorry to hear your story." They realised that the old lady was lonely. She allowed the children to take the framed photographs down and look at them. She said, "Both my boys went to your school when they were young." One older girl spoke up. She said to Grannie Gray, "Why not let the children of the village school be your children every Christmas. We could all send you a Christmas card, and bring you a little Christmas present."

As the children went home to their parents, they thought that this was a good idea. So that very Christmas, the Postman brought a lot of Christmas cards to Grannie Gray from the children of the Village school. Small presents such as handkerchiefs, a comb, note-paper, chocolate, a toothbrush, a teaspoon, pens, a book, a butterfly brooch, a book mark, a pencil sharpener, and a calendar, all came through Grannie Gray's letter box, from the children. Would you believe it, that evening, there was a little Christmas tree with lights on it in her window! The greatest surprise of all to the village people was when for the very first time, Grannie Gray came to the Candle-light Carol Service at the Church. The Vicar invited Grannie Gray to Christmas dinner, and she accepted. Everyone was beginning to understand that Christmas could be a happy time for older people as well as for children.

Prayer:

    Lord, we thank you for the joy at Christmas,
    which gives much pleasure to children.
    We pray for the older people at this festive season.
    Bless and keep them happy, as they remember their past.
    We pray for homes for elderly people, in need of nursing care.
    Make this a happy Christmas for each of them.   Amen.

Hymn:

    The Virgin Mary had a baby boy. (JP. 251)

Teachers' Note: (1) Here is a different slant on Christmas. Older people should not be forgotten at this time. (2) Both Simeon and Anna had a forward looking faith even in old age. (3) Children should learn "to give" as well as "to get". God so loved us that he gave his only Son.

(c) Bethlehem's Story   *Week 12   Looking Toward Christmas*

There were two kinds of people who came to see the Baby Jesus. First, there were the Shepherds. These were men and boys who spent their nights guarding their sheep on the hillside. Probably, they could not read or write. They were asleep in the fields, when they were awakened by the Angel of the Lord.

The shepherds were terrified as it was dark. "Do not be afraid", the Angel said, "Look, I bring you glad news of great joy for all the people. Today in the town of David, a Saviour has been born to you. He is Christ the Lord. I give you this sign; you will find the baby wrapped in swaddling clothes, and lying in a manger."

At that moment, a choir of Angels appeared, with the Angel of the Lord, praising God, and singing, "Glory to God in the Highest, and peace on earth. " When the angels had vanished, the Shepherds said, "Let us go down to Bethlehem and see what has happened". They hurried onwards and found Mary and Joseph, and the baby, who was lying in a manger. Afterwards, the shepherds told the story everywhere, but Mary kept the story in her mind and heart.

The second kind of people who came to see Jesus were the Wise Men from the East. We do not know how many Wise Men there were. The Bible does not say that there were "Three" Wise Men. It simply says that "there came Wise men from the East." Many years later, a Legend described the Wise men as "Kings" named Caspar, Melchior, and Balthasar.

We know that they brought three gifts. First, Gold, which was a gift for a King; Secondly, Frankincense, which was a sweet-smelling perfume used in the Temple Services. Thirdly, Myrrh, which was used to embalm dead people. These were strange presents to bring to a baby boy.

These Wise Men came to Jerusalem to the palace of Herod the King, because they had followed the new star. When this star had appeared, the Wise Men believed that it was the sign of the birth of a new King. So they had travelled a long way, probably on camels.

They arrived at Jerusalem, which was the wrong place. King Herod knew nothing about the birth of Jesus. So he asked his Bible scholars to tell him in which town the Bible had foretold that the Messiah should be born. The scholars answered that the Messiah (anointed one) would be born in Bethlehem. King Herod told the Wise men to find the child, and then to report back to him. The

Wise Men set off again to Bethlehem, but after finding the baby Jesus, they did not report back to King Herod, because they feared that he wanted to kill the baby.

On arriving at Bethlehem, they came to the place where Mary and Joseph were staying. They bowed down and worshipped the baby, as if he were a king, and gave to him their three gifts. Then they went home by a different route from that which they had come, to avoid telling King Herod anything.

What kind of a baby would Jesus have looked like? He was born in the Near East, so we may be sure that he would not have been born with white skin, or fair hair, or with blue eyes. Probably, he would have had black hair, brown eyes, and a brown skin like the Arab peoples of the world. The swaddling clothes wrapped around babies were just any piece of cloth that the mother could find, because people were very poor. His first cradle was a crib, or a manger as it is often called. This is the place for putting the hay into, when the cattle are being fed. It was probably filled with straw or hay to act as a mattress. There might have been sheep and lambs, or cows, or goats in the stable. The heat of the animals could have kept the baby warm, during the cold night. In bygone days they often kept the farm animals as close to the house as possible.

One would have expected that if Jesus was to be the King of the Jews, that he would have been born in a King's palace. Because he was born while on a journey, he had no warm and snug bed in which to lie. It was the kind hotel-keeper, who allowed the Holy family to stay in the stable, when the hotel was full.

In England in the large cities, there are many people who "sleep rough". This means that because they have no home, they sleep on park benches, or under bridges. They use cardboard boxes to keep warm. The Salvation Army and other organisations, such as "Shelter", have hostels for poor people. They also go out at night to give homeless people warm soup or a cup of tea and a sandwich.

Prayer:

Thank you God for sending the Lord Jesus
as a baby born in a stable.
We remember that the men of learning,
and the poor Shepherds worshipped Jesus.
We pray for all travelling people of the world,
and for those in our big cities who have no home.   Amen.

Hymn:

Away in a manger. (JP. 12)

Teachers' Note: (1) Educated people like the Wise men may serve Jesus Christ. (2) Ordinary people like the Shepherds always also need to worship. (3) Christmas is a time for the home. We must remember many people who have very poor homes, or no home at all.

Spring Term

(a) New Year Resolutions

It was the first week of the Winter term. The children walked to school on Monday morning. They had been talking about the presents they had received at Christmas time. They had attended a number of Christmas parties, so they talked about the fun they had, and the games they had played. Ian and Heather had parents who originally came from Scotland. They seemed to have celebrated something more than the other children, because they talked about how their family brought in the New Year.

Ian described how he and Heather were allowed to remain up late, until after twelve o'clock on Hogmanay! None of the other children knew what "Hogmanay" meant. So Ian and Heather explained that it was the Scottish name for the last day of the Old Year, the 31st. December. Heather explained that at their home, they cleaned the house from top to bottom. In the evening they wore their best clothes. Everyone stayed up to hear the clock strike twelve midnight, and to celebrate the passing of the Old year. They always sang Robert Burn's song, "Auld Lang Syne," and drank a toast to the New Year. She explained about the old Scottish superstition that the first person to put a foot over your doorstep must have dark hair, to have good luck through-out the New Year. If your first visitor had fair hair, and called to wish everyone, " A Happy New Year," then your visitor had to carry a piece of coal to present to the people of the house. The black coal was supposed to keep the bad luck away. "Of course, we do not really believe it!" Ian and Heather said. "It is only an old tradition, passed down by our grand-parents. There is no such a thing as bad luck, but accidents do happen."

By this time, the children had arrived at school, and soon the lines of pupils walked into their Assembly. The Head-teacher, Mr. Anderson, held a large drawing book, with fifty white pages in it. He opened the book at the first page, and put it down on a table at the front of the Assembly. He asked a teacher, Miss. Evans to go to his office and to find his fountain pen. The teacher quickly found the fountain pen lying open on his office desk. She brought the pen to Mr. Anderson in the Assembly. As she set the fountain pen down on the table, she accidentally made a large ink blot on the first page of the new book. Miss. Evans apologised for her mistake, and sat down.

Mr. Anderson did not seem to mind about the blot on the first page. Instead he smiled and asked the children whether he should just carry on drawing in the book, and ignore the blot, or whether he should tear out the page and begin again with a clean sheet of paper. All the children thought hard about this question. Then they held up their hands, and to the Headteacher's surprise, everyone agreed that he should tear the page out, and begin all over again, just as if the book was a new drawing book. So Mr. Anderson very carefully tore out the blotted page. The book now looked as unspoiled as it had been when it was new.

"Have you made any New Year resolutions, children" asked Mr. Anderson. No one answered. "New year resolutions, are just like tearing out a spoiled page in an exercise book, and beginning all over again", he said. "Let us make some New Year resolutions that will help us all through-out the New year. I will write them down, if you can tell me what they are." This is what they decided in the New Year assembly.

1. Mr. Anderson decided that he would try not lose his fountain pen any more.

2. Miss. Evans said that she would be more careful when carrying an ink pen.

3. Heather said that she would get up from her bed in the morning, the first time she was called by her Mum, and not wait for a second call.

4. Ian said that he would really wash his neck by himself every morning.

5. Lee who sometimes came to school late, said that he would try to come to school early.

6. Ann said that she would stop being such a chatterbox in class.

7. Dennis said that when he reached home after school, that he would stop throwing his coat and school-bag on the floor. He would hang them up in future.

8. Debbie was a bully sometimes in the school playground. She said that her New Year resolution was that she would stop hitting and pushing the younger children.

9. Mr Patel the school Caretaker who had been listening outside, put his head round the door, to everyone's surprise, and said, "This New Year I am going to try to smile at every boy or girl who speaks to me."

By this time, it was time to end the Assembly. Mr. Anderson said, "Well children, we must not make too many New Year resolutions in the Assembly, because we might forget some of them. Let us ask God to help us."

Prayer:

> Lord God we thank you for the New Year.
> Make it to be a happy year for all of us.
> Show us how to make,
> and keep our New Year resolutions.
> When we make genuine mistakes in future,
> help us to admit when we are wrong.   Amen.

Hymn:

> Travel on. (C&P.1 42)

Teachers' Note: (1) New Year resolutions are a good way to start the year with a clean sheet. (2) If we fail to keep our New Year resolutions, we need not be depressed because we can always try, try, and try again! (3) Keeping New Year resolutions helps us to control ourselves, and makes us to be strong willed. This is useful in sport or learning, for instance.

(b) A Second Chance   *Week 1   The New Year*

Children at school have two New Years. First, they begin the New School year in September. Secondly, they begin the calendar New Year, January 1st. This means that the New Year in January is really a second chance to do things better than before. We do not get many second chances in life.

Laura and Emma loved to go to the baths because they were good swimmers. Each time they went, they tried to improve their swimming. The Swimming Teacher one day asked them whether they would like to take up a Life-Savers course. It would mean that they would have to come to the pool one evening every week, in order to learn the skill of life saving. If they completed the course successfully, then they would be awarded a Certificate.

Laura and Emma talked the matter over with their parents and they decided to join the course. They faithfully attended the baths every Wednesday evening. They enjoyed it right from the first. They learnt a lot more about swimming and diving. Soon they were learning how to save the life of someone who fell into the water and could not swim. Then they learnt how to save a person from drowning who could swim, but was in difficulties, and had panicked in the water. They learnt how to give mouth to mouth resuscitation to anyone who had been saved from drowning. For this practice, they used "resuscitation Annie" blown up with an air pump. Then they were taught what to do if someone fell into an icy canal.

As the lessons continued through-out the year, Laura and Emma,sometimes felt that they would rather be at home watching the television. However, because they had given their word, they completed the course. Their parents came to the pool at the end of the course to see them receive the "Life-savers' Certificate." They were very proud of the two girls. They went back to school in September and the first term passed by very pleasantly.

Just after the New Year, they were going home from school, when some of the younger boys came rushing back to them. They were shouting that Ricki Burke had fallen through the ice on the pond near the golf links. Laura and Emma dropped their school bags and ran as fast as they could to the pond. Sure enough, there was Ricki Burke in the pond, hanging on to the ice. His hands and face were blue with cold, and he kept slipping under the water. Laura and Emma shouted to the older girls to 'phone for the ambulance and the fire-brigade. They knew that a fireman's ladder could reach the drowning boy.

Laura and Emma knew that they must not walk on the ice themselves and risk a further loss of life. They looked around, and noticed a wooden gate was lying in the grass near the opening in the hedge. Rushing over, they picked up the gate, and dragged it to the side of the pond. They pushed the wooden gate flat on top of the ice, and Emma crawled out on top of the gate, while Laura held her other hand. Emma nearly fell in as she caught hold of Ricki Burke by the hair, and kept his head above the water.

Laura then lay flat on her tummy, and also crawled out on the gate, and both girls very carefully dragged Ricki Burke out of the water on the the gate. The small boy had been badly cut on the ice, but worse than that, he had stopped breathing. Both Laura and Emma knew exactly what to do. The other children watched as they pumped his chest and blew into his mouth. After what seemed to be a long time the boy seemed to cough up water, and he opened his eyes.

Laura and Emma then began to move the boy's arms and legs, and at the same time, to rub them to bring the blood circulating through the boy's body again. The children heard the fire-engine and the ambulance sirens screaming, as vehicles drove over the grass on the golf course towards them. Even then Laura and Emma knew that they must not stop. Soon the ambulance men took over the task of exercising the boy's arms and legs. They wrapped a warm blanket around the boy. They put an oxygen mask over his mouth to help him breath, and whisked him off in the ambulance to the county hospital.

The Officer in charge of the fire-engine was very impressed with Laura and Emma's prompt action. He realised that his firemen were not needed on this occasion. He asked the girls their names, and as he wrote them down in his note-book, he said to them, "You girls have given Ricki Burke a second chance in life. I believe that you have saved his life. He will recover in hospital. Well done, Girls!" The girls went back to collect their school bags. They were ever so glad that they had spent their Wednesday evenings learning to become "Life-Savers." Lying in hospital, Ricki Burke closed his eyes, and was thankful that he had been given a second chance in life.

Prayer:

> Father God, we thank you for all the good people,
> who work in hospitals; in the ambulance service;
> in the police and fire -service.
> We thank you for all who teach "Life-Saving,
> at the swimming pool, or at the sea-side.
> Bless the young people who are learning to save lives.
> Make us all grateful for their skills.   Amen.

Hymn:

> Cross over the road. (C&P.l. 70)

Teachers' Note: (1) We ought to be thankful for second chances in life. (2) It is wise to learn to swim to save yourself. (3) It is wise to learn "Life-Saving to help others.

(c) A Testing Time   *Week 1   The New Year*

Every year will bring a testing time for each of us. We never know what the test will be until it arrives. The Jewish religion tells a story of how God cared for his people in history, when they were tested in the fire. Today, no one should ever attempt to play with fire.

Daniel and his three young friends were only lads, when an army under King Nebuchadnezzar, King of Babylon, surrounded the city of Jerusalem. The soldiers captured the city and took away Daniel and his three young friends as hostages to Babylon. The King wanted young men who had brains, and who were in good physical condition to be educated in the language and culture of Babylon. Daniel and his three Hebrew friends were chosen to be trained to become special servants in the King's court. For three years the four young men were to be sent to college. They also were commanded that for three years there were to eat food similar to the King, and to drink his wine before being presented at the King's court.

Daniel and his friends did not want to eat the king's food because they being Hebrews had special rules about the food they ate. They asked their guard to allow them to eat vegetables and drink water for ten days. After the ten days had passed, Daniel and his three friends looked healthier, and more fit than the other young men who had been eating the Kings food. So their guard allowed them to continue eating Hebrew food. At the end of three years, Daniel and his three friends appeared before the King. They had learnt most at the college, and God made them wiser than any of the other young men. They looked to be good leaders, so the King appointed them as members of his court. Daniel, with God's help, became an expert in interpreting the King's dreams.

Some time afterwards, King Nebuchadnezzar caused a statue, thirty-six metres high to be built. All the important people in the land went to the dedication ceremony of the gold statue. Officers, governors, councillors, and judges, all were there that day. At the sound of the King's royal music, everyone had to bow down and worship the gold statue. (Daniel was away at the court at the time) His three friends being Hebrews, refused to bow down to the statue. They said to the King, "We are Hebrews, and we will not bow down to any other God. We will not obey your command. Our God is able to save us from the flames, but even if he does not save us, we will not worship any other God."

The King was very angry, and ordered that the furnace should be made seven times hotter. The three young men were tied up and thrown into the blazing furnace. The fire was so hot, that it killed the soldiers who threw the three young men into the fire.

Nebuchadnezzar came to look at what was happening. He looked into the fire, and said, "I thought I ordered three men to be thrown into the fire, but I see four men walking through the flames, and the fourth man is like a God. When the three men came out of the fire, the ropes that tied them were gone. The flames had not harmed their clothes, or singed a hair of their heads. There was not even a smell of smoke on them. Nebuchadnezzar gave an order that no-one should ever speak a word against the God whom the three Hebrew men served. The three Hebrew men were promoted to high office in the kingdom.

Prayer:

> Lord, make us brave in this life.
> Help us not to do anything to bring shame
> upon ourselves, our families, or our school.
> Give us grace to know what is right,
> and always to do what is right.
> We thank you for our conscience,
> the voice inside us that tells us right from wrong.   Amen.

Hymn:

> When a knight won his spurs. (C&P.1 50)

Teachers' Note: (1) Eating a good diet keeps us healthy. (2) To pray to God is a very brave thing to do. (3) God will help us, if our test comes in the New Year, if we genuinely try to follow our conscience.

(a) Games Children Played Long Ago   *Week 2   Games and Rules*

Children nowadays own all sorts of toys. Computer games, Barbie dolls, and Cindy dolls, Trolls, Turtles, radio controlled racing cars and railways, battery driven cars and lorries, plastic games and toys of every description you can imagine. Years ago, in our great Grand-parents life-time, many children were very poor because their parents were unemployed. Many parents earned very low wages. Toys were expensive to buy. Many children had to make up their own games, either out of wood, or cloth, or even out of their imagination.

If a child could get a pen-knife, and a hammer and nails, then he could carve soft-wood into peg-men, or a boat, or even make a doll's house for his little sister. Children used to make rag dolls. Sometimes, they would cut out a Teddy Bear from cloth, and stuff it with saw-dust. They made a nose on the Teddy by sewing the face with black thread. Often they added buttons, which served for eyes.

In the street, if the policeman was not around, they would tie a rope around a lamp post, and swing around it, as if it were a Maypole. With a very long rope stretched across the street, children could together, and their Mums might even come out of the houses to join them!

The children played Hop Scotch on the pavement, chalking numbers on the concrete flagstones. They used a boot-polish tin, or a flat stone to throw on the number. Children rolled marbles down the street, since not many cars were parked outside houses. One did not need any toys to play leap frog. Many poor children would use empty shoe boxes to make a doll's bed, or a bigger box would make a doll's house. They put old pram wheels on a wooden soap box to make a trolley, and raced them down a steep road. The Scouts often held a trolley race, called a "Soap-Box Derby". Boys could race a trolley against the trolleys of their friends, as if they were real drivers racing in the "Grand Prix".

Sometimes young people would play cruel games on other people. To knock an old lady's door and then run away, is not a very kind action. Games that are hurtful to others are the games we ought not to play.

There was once a Shepherd boy who guarded his sheep and lambs on the hillside, overlooking a lovely village. One day the boy was feeling bored, so he decided to play a game on the Villagers. He ran down the hill-side into the village, shouting, "Wolf, Wolf, help, there's a Wolf!" The Villagers hearing the boy's cry for help, took up their weapons, and ran up the hillside, to chase the Wolf away. The Shepherd boy laughed at the Villagers. "There is no Wolf, I was only playing a trick on you," he said. The Villagers went home again.

A few days went by, and a second time the Shepherd boy ran down the hillside shouting "Wolf, Wolf, help, there's a Wolf". Again, the Villagers took their weapons and ran up the Hill-side to drive the Wolf away. Again, the Shepherd boy laughed at them, and said it was only a game. The Villagers were now very angry, that the boy was wasting their time. A Week passed by, and one day the Wolf really did come. The Shepherd boy ran down the hill-side shouting "Wolf, Wolf, help, Wolf." but not one of the Villagers bothered to listen to him.

The Wolf came slinking along by the side of the hedge, and carried away one of the little lambs in its teeth. The boy ran down the village street calling for help. No-one in the village believed a word the Shepherd boy said. The Villagers shouted, "Go away you foolish boy. You played that silly game on us once too often. You get what you deserved. You told us a pack of lies, and we do not believe you any more." The Shepherd boy never played that cruel game again.

Prayer:

> 0 Lord teach us to play games,
> that strengthen our our minds, and bodies.
> Above all show us that
> playing games gives us a sense of fair play.
> Keep us humble when we win.
> Show us how to be good losers.
> Help us always to be fair.   Amen.

Hymn:

> You can build a wall. (Break out). (C&P.2. 91)

Teachers' Note: (1) Games have rules which must be obeyed. (2) Games help to build our bodies, our minds, and our characters.(3) Games must unite us, not divide us. (4) We must learn to be humble when we win, and cheerful when we lose.

(b) Ring-a-Ring O' Roses   *Week 2   Games and Rules*

When we were very young children we may have played the game,

> Ring-a-Ring O Roses,
> A pocket full of posies,
> A-tishoo! A-tishoo,
> We all fall down.

The nursery rhyme has a happy meaning nowadays. Many people have explained the origin and meaning of this nursery rhyme, by tracing it back to the Great Plague of 1665-66. Many people fell sick and died of the disease. A rosy rash on the cheeks was the first indication that you had caught the infection. People are said, to have worn posies of herbs to keep off the germs. "A-tishoo", was the noise people made when sneezing, in the last stages of the illness, before they died. The line of the poem, "We all fall down" meant that people fell down, and died of this terrible sickness.

The epidemic broke out in London, where many people fell ill and died. At the time no-one realised that the sickness was carried by rats. The fleas on the backs of the rats spread the disease everywhere. Strangely enough, the disease seemed to fade away, after the "Great Fire" burned down most of the wooden houses in London. The fire must have destroyed the germs of the infection. So a simple younger children's game like Ring-0-Roses, because it is a happy game, has helped us to forget a sad part of our history.

If you ever go to Derbyshire, which is a very beautiful hilly part of England, you will enjoy seeing the Well-dressing. Before the days when water was put through pipes to our homes, most of the villages had public wells. The people brought their buckets to the village well for water. The people still decorate the wells annually. First, they put soft clay on a flat board. Then, they press thousands of flower petals into the soft clay to make a beautiful pictures of many colours. The Derbyshire wells have been "dressed" with these magnificent pictures for hundreds of years. Many of the pictures show Bible stories.

If you ever get the opportunity, you should visit the village of Eyam. This village was once infected by the Black Plague. In 1665, one of the men who was engaged in the cloth industry, brought home a bale of cloth from London. The cloth was damp, so he opened the roll up, in order to dry it out in front of the fire. Unknown to him, the infected fleas were in the cloth. Soon he, and his wife and family were all dead from the sickness. Worse still, the disease spread throughout the village. Soon, 257 men, women, and children lay dying.

Two Eyam Ministers, the Rev. William Mompesson and the Rev. Thomas Stanley decided to cut the village off from the outside world. They organised the houses into cottage hospitals. No-one was allowed to enter or leave the village, while the Plague was active. Food was brought in from outside, and the villagers paid for it, by leaving their money in a pot of water mixed with vinegar as disinfectant. The payment pot was put on a stone near the village well. Someone from the outside world collected the money. To this day the Black Plague is remembered in pictures of flower petals by the Eyam village well, and the Church. The last Sunday of August is remembered as "Plague Sunday." On that day, long ago, Catherine the Rector's wife died. The plague slowly left the village. People were thankful.

The nursery rhyme -'Ring-a-Ring 'O Roses is a very happy game for younger children to play. Its happiness helps us to forget the sadness behind it.

Prayer:

Lord, we thank you for our happy games.
We thank you for the stories,
about the children and their parents,
who lived long ago.
Help us each one, to live in goodness and kindness,
that children of the future may be pleased,
when they are told tales about us.   Amen.

Hymn:

Guess how I feel. (C&P.2. 89)

Teachers Note: (1) People usually do not fall ill through any fault of their own. Good people may fall sick. (2) Cleanliness prevents disease. (3) We should realise that Doctors, and Nurses, are doing God's work of Healing in the world today.

(c) Fair Play   *Week 2   Games and Rules*

All games have rules. Unless you keep the rules of the game, the game will not work out. Anyone who does not keep the rules of a game is a "Cheat". No-one likes a cheat! The most important rule in every game is "Fair Play." Strangely, no-one needs to be taught what "Fair play" means. Everyone of us knows inside our own selves what it means to play fair. Older people call it "justice".

Elizabeth was coming down the road to school on her mountain bike, when her front tyre became very soft. Tom was nearly late for school, when he also came down the road on his mountain bike. He stopped, and quickly took his air-pump from his own bike, and blew up Elizabeth's front tyre. They both arrived at school just on time. A few weeks passed by, and Tom was coming down the road to school on his bike. His tyre had gone down. He found that the little air-valve in the rim of the wheel was loose, and this was causing the air to escape from the tyre. Tom realised that he had left his air-pump at home in the garage. What could he do!

Just at that moment Elizabeth came riding on her bike down the road to school. "Please, lend me your pump", Tom shouted, "My tyre is nearly flat." Elizabeth , was feeling rather cold, because it was a frosty morning. "0 I can't be bothered to stop this morning, I'm too cold!" she shouted. Tom knew that he must not ride his bike on a flat tyre, because it would do damage. He pushed his bike all the way to school, and arrived late in class. Do you think that Elizabeth played fairly that morning? Do you think that Tom would stop on another morning to help Elizabeth, if her tyre went flat a second time? I think Tom would help Elizabeth a second time, because he was not a mean person! Every-day life is like a game. Keeping the rules makes everyone happy. There is an old proverb which says, "A friend in need, is a friend indeed."

Grown-up people also may cheat, or act very unfairly. Jesus told a story about a King who employed a man as his Servant. The King was the man's Master. After a period of time, the King asked His Servant to pay back his debts. The Servant owed the King a vast amount of money, that ran into millions of pounds. Because the Servant was not able to pay the money back on time, the King ordered the Servant, his wife, and his children to be sold as slaves. His house also, and everything that the Servant owned, was to be sold to repay the debt.

The Servant fell on his knees before the King. "Please, be patient with me, Master," he begged, "and I will pay you back everything I owe you." The King took pity on his Servant, and cancelled the debt. He forgave the Servant all the millions of pounds he owed him. The King's Servant went home a free man, happy because he did not owe any money.

Now this same King's Servant also had a Fellow-Servant who owed him a few hundred pounds. It was nothing like the millions once owed by the King's Servant to his Master. The King's Servant was a very greedy and cruel person. He caught his Fellow-Servant by the throat. He demanded, "Pay me back what you owe me." The Fellow-Servant fell on his knees, and begged the King's Servant, saying, "Be patient with me, and I will pay you back."

The King's Servant refused to wait even a short time. Instead he had his Fellow- Servant thrown into prison until he could pay the debt. When the other Servants heard what had happened, they were very sorry for the man in prison. They went and told the King what had happened. The King became very angry when he heard. He sent for the King's Servant. He said to the cruel man, " I took pity on you. I cancelled all the debt you owed me, because you asked me. I forgave you everything. How can you be so unfair? Should you not have had mercy on your Fellow-Servant, in the same way that I had mercy on you? The King handed his cruel Servant over to the Jailers, and he was cast into prison, until he could pay the debt. The King had been very angry with his Servant because he was not playing fair in life.

Prayer:

> Father God, teach us that you require from each of us,
> fair play and justice in this life.
> Teach us to be the friend of all,
> and the enemy of no-one.
> Because you, Lord have been good to us,
> help us to be fair to other people.   Amen.

Hymn:

> Make us worthy Lord. (Mother Teresa's prayer). (C&P.2. 94)

Teachers' Note: (1) Playing fair in a game, teaches us self discipline. (2) Everyone knows inside themselves when they are being selfish. (3) Fair play is built on the idea that one good turn deserves another! The story is found Matthew 18.v 23-35.

(a) Being Thoughtful   *Week 3   Being a Thinking Kind of Person*

The theme this week is about being a thinking kind of person. Today, you are going to hear three short stories. Try to see what links them all together.

First, there was a large iron cover over the school drain in the playground. The iron cover was round. It had been cracked into two pieces, by a heavy lorry running over it, when it was delivering the oil for the school heater. The Headteacher, telephoned the school works department, and reported the matter, because he did not want any of the children to trip on the drain.

The next day, workmen arrived in a van with the new drain cover. It was play time. All the children gathered inside the railings to see the workmen fit the new drain cover over the drain-hole. When the workmen carried the new heavy iron cover into the play-ground, all the children began to laugh. The workmen wondered why the children were laughing. The workmen were carrying a new square-shaped cover. The children knew that the drain was round like a circle.

The Head-teacher heard the children laughing, so he came out to see the workmen, who were standing scratching their heads. The Head-teacher smiled and said to the workmen, " Do you not know that you cannot put a square peg in a round hole." The workmen also saw the funny side of things, and they too began to laugh, as they carried the square drain cover back to the works van.

The second story is about Rachel, who was ten years old. She was quite tall for her age. One morning her mother had to go to town early. Mother told Rachel that she might not be home until five o'clock in the afternoon. Mother said, "The front door key is in the table drawer, Rachel, take it with you, and when you arrive back from school, just open the door yourself." Rachel, was a very dependable girl, and could be trusted by her mother. After her mother had gone to town in the bus, Rachel opened the table drawer, and found that there were many keys there. She took the big key, and slipped it into her pocket, and went off to school.

In the afternoon, as she came home from school, Rachel took the key out of her pocket and tried to open the front door. The key went into the keyhole alright, but it would not turn. Rachel, could not get into the house. It began to rain, so she went to the neighbour's house next door, and asked Mrs. Adams, whether she could shelter in her house out of the rain, until five o'clock, when her mother would be home again.

Mrs. Adams was a kind lady, and welcomed Rachel into her house. She gave Rachel a glass of hot orange squash and a bun, to warm her up, because she looked to be cold. At five o'clock, Mother arrived back from town. Rachel came in from the house next door, and told Mother that the key would not open the front door. Mother smiled at Rachel, and said, "Do you not know that you cannot open the front door with the back door key?"

The third story is about Ben. In the class one day, he told the Teacher that there were thousands of cats on his garden wall. Miss. Dobson, the Teacher said, "Now, Ben, there are not thousands of cats on your garden wall!" Ben replied , "Well, there are hundreds of cats on our garden wall." Again, Miss. Dobson said, "Now, Ben, there are not hundreds of cats on your garden wall!." Ben replied, "Well, there is our cat, and the the cat from next door on the garden wall." Miss. Dobson said, "Yes, Ben, we all believe you when tell us that there are two cats on the yard wall. You sometimes exaggerate! That means your words do not fit correctly, with what you see. You are really telling lies."

Can you see the link between all the stories? Someone chose a square cover for a round hole. Someone tried to fit a back-door key into the front door. Someone told lies about the number of cats. The meaning for us is that if we are thinking kind of people, we will see that some things fit together, and some things do not. Being a thinking kind of person, helps us to understand, that there are two things that always must go together. These two things are our "Words", and the "truth". If we make a promise, then we must keep that promise. When we tell a lie, it means that our words and what is true are not the same thing. If we say that we are sorry, then we must really mean it, and change our ways. We must be thoughtful and honest.

Prayer:

> Father God, help us to do what we say.
> Show us that our words and our actions,
> to be truthful, must fit together.
> Help us always to be truthful.
> Forgive us if we have told lies,
> or if we have avoided telling the truth.   Amen.

Hymn:

> Who put the colours in the rainbow? (C&P.l 12)

Teachers' Note: (1) Children ought to learn to think about their actions because it is a sensible thing to do. (2) Children ought to be thinking kind of people, because it is being honest with ourselves, and that is how we learn. (3) Children who are truthful are respected by others.

(b) The Lady with the Lamp   *Week 3 Being a Thinking Kind of Person*

Florence Nightingale was a very thoughtful person. As you now hear her story, try and think about, how Florence shows her thoughtfulness. She was born in Florence, a town in Italy, in the year 1820, while her rich parents were on a journey through Europe. Her parents owned three family houses, one in London, one near the New Forest, and one in Derbyshire, (where they spent their Summer holidays). Florence never went to school, but was taught at home by governesses. When she reached the age of twelve, her Father, who was a very learned man, took over her education at home. She had an older sister.

Florence as a young girl loved to learn languages, and mathematics. She played with her dolls, and loved to pretend that they were unwell. Although Florence was rich, she saw many poor and sick people everywhere in England. When she was sixteen, Florence, felt that she had been called by God to do some special service. What that service would be, she did not know. She became a young lady, and was able to go to all the fashionable places with other rich young ladies, such as dancing, the theatre, dinners, and concerts. She was able to travel abroad. One gentleman wanted to marry her, and he waited for seven years for Florence to agree. However, Florence in the end decided not to marry the rich gentleman.

When Florence was 30 years old, she decided to become a Nurse. In those days, hospitals were horrible dirty places. Nurses were people who were not trained, as our nurses are trained today. The beds were not kept clean. Doctors performed operations without any anaesthetics or drugs. Many people died because their wounds were not kept clean. When Florence's parents heard that she was going to become a nurse they were very angry, and they did everything they could to put Florence off the idea. Florence went to Kaiserwerth, Germany, to get some real nursing training, as there was none in England

When Florence came back to England, she took a position as Superintendent over a Home for gentlewomen. The trouble was that she did not receive any wages. Her Father, being a rich man, gave her an allowance of five-hundred pounds per year on which to live. She made the Home clean up their wards. She arranged for a bell to be put beside the beds of the patients, so that they could call the Nurses, when they needed them. A hot water system was installed in the wards. Food was properly cooked. Above all she set out to train the Nurses about hygiene. She organised jam-making to raise some money for the hospitals.

When the Crimean War began against Russia, the British Army was sent to the Crimea in 1854. Sadly, the British soldiers endured terrible suffering, because there were very few medical supplies. The soldiers died more from diseases than from bullet wounds. Florence and thirty-eight other women went out to Scutari, in Turkey to work in an army barracks which had been used as a hospital. It was a gloomy, filthy, very damp building.

Florence set about organising the barracks into a clean hospital. She began a laundry to wash the sheets and pillow-cases used by the sick soldiers. She cleaned-up the kitchens, and a French Chef provided warm well-cooked meals.

She wrote letters back home to England for the sick soldiers. She sat by the bedside of soldiers who were dying. The corridors of the barracks were nearly four miles in length. Every evening Florence used to walk these corridors with her lantern, visiting the sick men. (There was no electric light in those days). This is why she was known among the soldiers as, "The Lady with the Lamp." Queen Victoria sent her a beautiful gold and diamond brooch, with the words on it, "Blessed are the merciful".

When the war was over, she came back to England. The authorities arranged brass bands, and committees to welcome her home. Florence did not want any such fuss. She travelled quietly and unknown to anyone, under the assumed name of Miss. Smith. She got out of the train in Derbyshire, and walked into her own house again, surprising the family.

Florence, because she was a thinking kind of person, she was not a proud person. She was determined to get help for the soldiers hospitals. She conducted a campaign among the public to improve medical care in the armed forces, and in hospitals generally. Her helper was Sidney Herbert, who set up a commission to examine the Army Medical Services.

Florence herself became ill, and for the rest of her life, she was an invalid, often confined to bed. Florence had a number of cats, which she loved very much. Although she did not like many visitors, the cats were always welcome on her bed. She died in 1910, a kind and thinking kind of person to the very end. People like Florence, think about improving matters, and then work to make their ideas real.

Prayer:

> Lord, we give you our praise for people,
> such as Florence Nightingale.
> We are grateful for all the men and women,
> who are Nurses in our hospitals.
> Bless those whose work is caring for the sick.
> We thank you for their knowledge and skills,
> and their kindness and helpfulness,
> when we are ill in hospital.   Amen.

Hymn:

> Join with us. (C&P.l. 30)

Teachers' Note: (1) Thinking kind of people want to live useful lives. (2) Thinking people have ideas that lead other people to make improvements in life. (3) Thinking people usually they have a deep inner strength of character.

(c) The Tax Collector *Week 3 Being a Thinking Kind of Person*

Sometimes dishonest people can be very thoughtful people. There was a very rich man called Zacchaeus. He lived in Jericho. The Roman Army had invaded the land. Zacchaeus was very good at counting money, so he began to work for the Roman authorities. This is how he became even richer. He was the tax-collector, and very often tax collectors were dishonest people. They charged the people more taxes than they should have done, and they kept the extra money for themselves. The ordinary people hated tax collectors because they were often dishonest men.

When Jesus was passing through Jericho, Zacchaeus wanted to get a good look at Jesus. The problem was that he was a very small man, and he could not see over the crowd. However, he was a very resourceful person, and soon he had a good idea. He climbed up a sycamore tree, near the roadside, so that when Jesus was passing, surrounded by the crowd, Zacchaeus could look down from a branch, and get a good view of Jesus.

When Jesus reached the tree, he looked up, and saw Zacchaeus up in the tree. He called out to Zacchaeus, "Come down, I would like to go to your house for a meal." Zacchaeus climbed down from the tree in a hurry. He took Jesus to his house as his special guest. Everyone was shocked that Jesus had gone to be the guest of a man who was a cunning cheat with money.

However, Zacchaeus was so impressed by the words of Jesus, that he became a changed man. He realised that in future his everyday behaviour would have to change for the good. Zacchaeus said to Jesus, " Lord, I am going to give half of everything I own to the poor people. If I have cheated anybody out of anything, then I will pay him back, four times the amount which I have taken." Jesus said to him, "Today, God's way of life has come to your house."

Can you see that for a long time Zacchaeus was a cheat, and a thief. His words did not fit his actions. His Tax Account books were false. The moment Zacchaeus decided to become a good man, in the presence of Jesus, he also changed his way of life. He became an honest man again. He began to put his new beliefs into action.

This is why we always must try to be honest in our work at school. Answers in maths should be honest answers. We should always tell the truth. When we cheat, we are telling lies to ourselves, as well as to other people. Are you a thinking kind of person?

Prayer:

      Lord we thank you that the words of Jesus,
      changed a man such as Zacchaeus,
      from cheating people to being honest.

May we never be cheats, and deceive people.
May we never steal what rightfully belongs
to someone else. Keep us all honest.   Amen.

Hymn:

Go tell it on the mountain. (C&P.l. 24)

Teachers's Note: St. Luke Ch. 19. (1) Zacchaeus overcame his problem of not being able to see over the crowds, by thinking about the problem. (He climbed a tree.) (2) Zacchaeus overcame his evil reputation of being a thief, by restoring to people the money he had stolen. (3) Zacchaeus became a man who Jesus admired and respected. Bad people can change, and genuinely become reformed characters.

(a) The Traffic Lights

Week 4   Light

Gareth's Dad was an electrician. He worked for the Highway Department of the Borough Council. He helped to repair the street lamps. He could also repair the fuses when the lights in the Town Hall went out. One day his works department received a radio-telephone call, from the police Panda car, asking for help. The Police officer said, "F for Freddie calling. Car 4F calling! Is that the Highway works department! The London Road is blocked with cars, buses, and trucks, because something has gone wrong with the traffic lights at High Street. Can you help? Over and out!" Gareth's Dad answered back immediately, "Highways Department calling Car 4F for Freddie. We are on our way. Over and out!"

His little green van went up the side streets, avoiding the traffic on the main street. He was soon at the cross-roads junction on the High Street. He jumped out quickly and saw that the traffic was in a muddle. None of the traffic lights were working. All the trucks, buses, and cars, were crawling slowly, because no driver would give way, either to the cars on the right, or to left. Gareth's Dad opened the metal fuse box on the side of the footpath, and found that the fuses had blown. He took the old fuses out, and put in a set of new fuses. As if by magic, all the traffic lights began to work correctly again. The traffic began to go through the lights easily, and the London Road was clear again.

"Do you know what order the traffic lights take, Gareth?" his Dad said that evening after school. Gareth tried to say the order, two or three times. Somehow, he always said it incorrectly. Dad then told Gareth it was, "Green, Amber, Red, then Red and Amber, then Green again." "Go down and look for yourself."he said. Gareth went down to see the traffic lights, and sure enough, his Dad was right. The order was "Green, Amber, Red, then Red and Amber, and then Green.

Dad said, "Green means, 'Go'." There is a time in everyone's life, when they should be adventurous and go. Amber means "Stop and use caution. There are times when we ought to take special care." Red means 'Stop.' There are times in life when people should stop what they are doing."

It was the local Chess Competition, but it was a freezing cold night. A warm fire, and a good television programme made it difficult for Gareth to decide whether to stay at home, or to go out to the competition. All at once he jumped up, and said to his Dad, "I'll go," and off he went. Gareth came home smiling. He said, "Dad, I'm glad I decided to go to-night, because I beat the Police Sergeant at Chess."

Next day was Saturday, and Gareth and his Dad usually went to the local football match. It was half-past-two in the afternoon, and they were in a hurry. All at once Gareth stopped his Dad. Look, old Mrs. Becket's milk bottle is still outside her front door. Let us go round the back door, and see if she is alright. Gareth and his Dad, went into the back garden, and looked into Mrs. Becket's window. There she was, lying on the floor. The back door was unlocked, so they went in to her little cottage. They lifted the old lady up, and helped her into her arm-chair.

They 'phoned the District Nurse, who quickly arrived at the cottage. They were all relieved that Mrs.Becket was alright, and none the worse for her experience, except for a slight bruise on her arm. Nurse thanked Gareth for taking care to notice that the milk bottle was still on the door-step in the afternoon. Dad and Gareth went off to the foot-ball game a little late, but very happy.

On the way home, they passed a small river. An empty glass bottle was floating on the water, and some lads were trying to break it, by throwing stones at the bottle. Gareth's Dad smiled at the lads, and called them over. He explained that if they broke the bottle, it would fall into the river, and spoil the environment. Maybe in the Summer when children paddled, someone would get their feet cut by the broken glass. The lads had never thought of that before. They stopped throwing the stones at the bottle, and pulled it to the bank of the river. Picking the bottle up, they put it in a waste bin in the street.

That night, Dad said to Gareth, "Did you notice the Green, Amber, and Red lights in any part of this week." Gareth smiled at his Dad. He understood what Dad meant. Now children, "Can you see which story represents the Green light; which story represents the Amber light; and which story represents the Red light?"

Prayer:

> Lord, when we see the Green light in life,
> help us to go into action in some good task.
> When the Amber light of conscience warns us,
> make us careful, thoughtful and cautious.
> When the Red light in life commands us to stop,
> our foolish or wrongful actions.
> Help us to do so.   Amen

Hymn:

> Light up the fire. (C&P.l 55)

Teachers' Note: (1) There is always a time for action. (2) Caution and consideration is always wise. (3) There are times to stop and to change our ways.

(b) Candle-Light

Week 4   Light

People long ago learnt that oil can burn. They made oil lamps, with a piece of wick placed in the oil. The wick might have been a piece of rope. Soon, it was learned how to thicken the oil, and make it solid. People then made candles.

THE CARRIAGE CANDLE. During Queen Victoria's reign, there were many horsedrawn carriages. Each horse-drawn vehicle had a light at the front, and one at the back. Often these lamps were made in the shape of a square glass and metal box, with a long brass stem to hold a candle in it. The front lamp had a clear glass, and the back lamp had red glass in it. So people could see in the dark, whether the carriage was coming or going. The candles did not blow out, because the candle was protected from the wind by the glass. We call this candle, "The Carriage candle", because it was used by people who worked with carriages or any horse-drawn cart. Children sometime had the job of keeping the lamp windows clean.

THE NIGHT LIGHT. This candle is very short. It was put in a saucer of water at night, perhaps, beside the bed of some sick person, in the days before there were any gas, or electric lights. Many people today keep one or two of these candles in a cupboard, in case the electricity might be cut off.

THE PRAYER CANDLES. Many church congregations use candles in their worship. The candle flame goes upward, and reminds us that prayer rises to God. The flame reminds us to keep our faith shining bright. The Bible tells us that King Solomon's Temple had ten golden candle sticks in it. These candlesticks were really single oil lamps, with seven lights burning from each one, at the same time.

THE BIRTHDAY CAKE CANDLES. Not all candles are about work and worship. Some candles are about joy and birthdays. It is fun to have a birthday, and to invite some of your friends to your birthday party at home. When the birthday cake is brought in, with a number of candles alight on it, you have the honour of trying to blow them all out at once. Candles and lights at Christmas celebrate the birthday of the baby Jesus.

Did you know that light attracts? Have you ever watched a moth fly around a candle or a lamp. Have you ever heard of Blackpool illuminations? People travel in cars coaches, and trains to Blackpool, just to see the lights along the promenade. There is something attractive about lights.

Long, long ago, there was once a young man who did not behave very well in his own home. He used to argue, and slam doors in temper. He rebelled against his old parents. They lived in a beautiful cottage in the country. His nasty behaviour broke his parents' heart. One day he packed his bags and decided to leave home for ever.

His parents were very sad. They said to their son, "We are very sorry that you are leaving us. We want you to remember that you will always be welcome to return back to our cottage here. We are going to put a candle inside a little lamp, and put the lamp in the window every evening. This will be a sign that we still love you, and that our home is your home. You can always be sure that you can come home again."

The careless young man just walked out the door without saying "Good-bye" to his old parents. He went to sea, and sailed the world for years. He never wrote home. After seven years, the young man fell ill, and he thought to himself,"I might die far away from my home. If God makes me well again, then I will return and visit my old parents."

The young man became well again, and sailed back to England. He boarded a train which took him to his village station. It was getting dark as he made his way down the country road, towards his cottage home. He wondered to himself, whether his parents might have died. He had been away such a long time. Perhaps, they were so disgusted with his conduct that they would not want him home again. Perhaps, they had moved to another town. As he made his way round the bend of the country road, it was pitch dark. He saw a cottage, and an old lady was pulling the curtains. As she did so, to his heart-felt joy, she put a little lamp with a candle in it, into the window. Its light flickered out into the darkness.

The young man's steps quickened. He knocked the brass knocker, and two old people came to the door. They could not believe their eyes. Their long lost son had come home again. They hugged him, and kissed him with joy. They made him a hot meal, because he was hungry and cold. The old man opened his Bible, and he read from St. Luke's Gospel, chapter 15. "This my son was lost and is

84

found. He was dead and his alive again. Come let us rejoice." The son was now a better and wiser man. They became a very happy family again.

Prayer:

> Lord we thank you for the lights of the sky;
> for the Sun, the Moon, and thousands of stars.
> We thank you for all the candles of our world,
> which bring meaning to people everywhere.
> We thank you for Jesus Christ,
> who said, "I am the light of the world".   Amen.

Hymn:

> Give me oil in my lamp. (C&P.1 43)

Teachers' Note: (1) Candles are associated with work, worship, sickness, birthdays, and Christmas. (2) Light is very useful and attractive. (3) Light reminds us of the love shown by the old parents. It also reminds us of Jesus, who said, "I am the light of the world. His pure life was like a shining light in a world of darkness.

(c) The Lost Coin *Week 4   Light*

Jesus told the story of a lady who was happily married. In those days a married lady wore a string of little coins around her head, just as married ladies today wear a wedding ring on their finger. This lady had ten little silver coins tied by a cord around her forehead. She was very proud of these silver coins, because her husband had given them to her, years ago, on her wedding day.

One day when she took off the string of silver coins, to her dismay, she found that she had lost one silver coin. There were only nine coins remaining, instead of ten. The lady was troubled, because when her husband came home, he might think that she had been careless. She used a brush to sweep the floor, looking for her silver coin. The floors in those days were dry mud floors. The lady took a candle, and lit it. Houses sometimes only had one opening in the wall, acting as window, so the inner room was rather dark. Using the lighted candle, she searched very diligently, among the straw on the mud floor, until she found the silver coin again.

Now, she was full of joy and happiness because she had found the silver coin. She called all her neighbours around her, and she said to them, "Friends, come rejoice with me, for I have found the silver coin which I had lost." All her neighbours began to rejoice along with her. She put the candle away. Then she carefully sewed the little coin back on the string, beside the other nine. She placed the ten coins around her head, and she took care never to lose any one of them again!

The candle was very useful in this story. Sometimes a Dentist shines a light inside your mouth to look closely at your teeth. A Policeman on his night beat, often shines his torch into the dark corners of the street. A fire brigade tender attending a house on fire, sometimes uses a searchlight to help the firemen see the water-main at night. Even boats at sea need lights. Light-houses, which show up the dangerous rocks along the coast to ships at sea, are very useful.

Young people are like lights, when they are useful, or when they help their friends. When John loses his lunch money in the playground, and Susan finds it, then Susan is like a searching light. When Trevor picks up broken glass on the football field, and puts it in the waste bin, then he is like a warning light. What kind of a light are you?

Prayer:

> O Lord, we thank you for the stories we hear in Assembly.
> We thank you for the parables which Jesus told.
> Assist us to see the meaning in each story.
> May we too, learn to live useful and helpful lives.
> May the truth always shine in us,
> like a candle, which never goes out.   Amen.

Hymn:

> From the darkness came light. (C&P.l. 29)

Teachers' Note: (1) This story is found in St. Luke chapter 15. It is a parable told by Jesus. (The lost sheep: the lost coin: the lost son.) (2) The candle may be likened to the Church, or to the Holy Spirit. (3) To be "lost" is to be out of touch. Many people may be out of touch with religious things. The ten coins symbolise unity and friendship.

(a) Listening to Others   *Week 5   Donkey Tales*

The was once a Miller and his Son, who decided to sell their donkey at the market in town. They walked alongside the donkey down the road. They met some people who said, "How foolish these two Millers are. They are walking this long road to market, when one of them could be having a ride on the donkey."

The Miller thought that this was a good idea. So he allowed his Son to ride the donkey.

A few miles along the road, they met some farmers. The farmers said to the Miller, "How can you allow that lazy Son of yours to ride that donkey? You'll make him even more lazy." So the Miller took the advice of the farmers, and he made his Son get off the donkey. He himself sat on the donkey's back, as they made their way along the road to market.

A few more miles down the road, they met some farmers wives, who said," Look at that selfish Miller riding the donkey, while his Son has to walk on his own weary feet." Hearing these words, the Miller, took his Son up behind him on the saddle. They both set off again to ride to market.

Further on, they met several shepherds on the road. The shepherds said, "You two lazy Millers are going to wear out this poor animal. The donkey will look so tired when he gets to market, that no one will want to buy him. We think that you two strong Millers should carry him".

So the Miller and his Son climbed down from the donkey's back. They tied the donkey's legs together. Then both the Miller and his Son carried the donkey, slung on a pole between them. The other travellers on the road to market began to laugh at them. They looked so ridiculous, because they had heeded all the advice they had been given. Foolishly, they had not used their own brains to decide what to do.

Worse events were to happen. The donkey felt so uncomfortable, that it began to kick and wriggle to get free. They were crossing a bridge over a river, when suddenly the ropes holding the struggling donkey broke. The donkey fell over the bridge into the river and was drowned. The Miller and his Son went home sadder and wiser people. They realised that in trying to please everyone, they had pleased no-one. Worst of all, they had lost their valuable donkey.

The lesson the Millers learned that day, was that you cannot please everyone, no matter what you do. It is better to use your own mind, and try to do what you honestly think is the best. If you make up your own mind, then you will have no-one to blame but yourself.

Prayer:

> Lord, we thank you for schools and for Teachers.
> Help us to realise that our Teachers teach us,
> in order that we may learn to decide for ourselves.
> Grant that we may not try to please everyone,
> but only do what we know is wise, and good. Amen.

Hymn:

The journey of life. (C&P.l. 45)

Teachers' Note: (1) We have to learn the important difference between knowledge and opinion. (2) Teachers may give us knowledge, but others may only tell us what they prefer. (3) Until we are old enough to choose for ourselves, we ought to think carefully about what our Parents advise us to do.

(b) The Donkey that Ran Away   *Week 5   Donkey Tales*

Emma was eight years old. On her ninth birthday, her father and mother bought her a little grey donkey. She called it "Jock" because it originally came from a farm in Scotland. Jock the donkey was quite tame and well behaved. Emma lived in a cottage in the country. She was fortunate because there was a small field behind their cottage. Jock had his stable at the bottom of the field. Emma soon learned to ride the donkey around the field.

When Emma was at school, and her parents were at work, the donkey sometimes felt quite lonely. He could see the hills in the distance, and the tall trees blowing in the wind. He could smell the sea, which was not far away. Jock used to wonder what lay down the narrow road that led past the cottage. After a time, Jock became a discontented donkey, and he kept raising his nostrils to smell whatever scents the wind blew across his field.

When Emma and her parents had gone out one Summer evening, the gate of the field was blown slightly ajar by the wind. Jock squeezed out through the gate, and he was on the road, at last! He felt that he was now free to see the world for himself. Off he trotted up the narrow road. The cars and lorries gave him a fright, when they blew their horns at him. He tried to keep off the road and walk along the grassy verge. He trotted into one open field and ended up walking along the sea shore.

Some children were delighted to see him, and they thought that maybe they could get a ride on his back. Jock was a little frightened and ran away. Back on the road again, he wandered slowly towards the church. He looked over the wall, and he saw an old graveyard and a new graveyard. In the old graveyard, the grass was growing very long between the gravestones. Over the wall, in the new graveyard, the grass had been mown very short. There was no-one about, so the little donkey wandered all over the place. Then the Vicar appeared. He gently came up to Jock and led him by the harness away down the road. He knew that Emma owned the little grey donkey.

Emma and her parents had just arrived home. They were very concerned that Jock had left the enclosed field. They were very worried that he might be knocked down on the road. When the Vicar brought the donkey round the back of the cottage, they smiled, and thanked him.

The Vicar explained how he had found the stray donkey. Then he said, "I have just had a wonderful idea. The Church Wardens and I have been wondering how to raise money to buy a new lawn mower to cut the long grass in the old graveyard. None of the graves have been used for many years. Emma, we could pay you a small amount of money, if during the late Spring, Summer, and early Autumn you would allow your donkey to graze in our old graveyard. There is a high wall, and a heavy iron gate there. There would be no danger of Jock getting on to the road."

Emma, exclaimed, " A donkey grass cutter! That is a splendid idea. Jock would never be hungry!" Mum and Dad agreed with the arrangement. Jock could not tell them, but he was delighted too! Now he would see more of the world, and of other people. In Winter Jock was kept cosy and warm in his stable behind the cottage. Everyone remarked how tidy the old graveyard had become.

People attending church would often look over the wall, and give Jock a pat on the head. He became a favourite. Once a year, at the Service on Palm Sunday, Emma led her donkey with the children walking behind her. Each child carried Palm leaves. They processed along the aisle of the Church. After that, Emma's donkey never ran away again!

Prayer:
> Lord we thank you for the world of animals.
> Help us to be kind to our pets at home.
> We thank you for birds that fly in the sky.
> We thank you for fish that swim in the sea;
> for farm animals, that graze in the fields.
> We thank you for Vets, and for farmers.   Amen.

Hymn:
> From the tiny ant. (C&P.2 79)

Teachers' Note: (1) Animals are as much part of our environment as trees, rivers, and the countryside. (2) Household pets are not toys that can be cast aside. They need love and care all the time. (3) Wild animals are happiest when they are free to enjoy their habitat.

(c) A Donkey's Adventure

Week 5   Donkey Tales

The was once a donkey which was owned by a very good and kindly Samaritan traveller. The Samaritan and his donkey often travelled to the city of

Jerusalem. The road was an up-hill road. The Samaritan and his donkey often travelled in the opposite direction, down the same road to the city of Jericho. The road went down-hill through a deep hot valley, before it reached Jericho.

There were two problems. When the Samaritan went to Jerusalem on business, he knew that he was unpopular there. The Jewish people did not like people from Samaria. The second problem was that travelling up and down this particular road was dangerous, because there were bands of robbers in hiding, ready to attack any unwary traveller. However, life must go on, and so the Samaritan and his donkey went up and down the road from time to time.

It happened that one day when the Samaritan was making a journey on his donkey down to Jericho, that another traveller, who was a Jew, was also on the same road, some distance ahead. This second traveller, was attacked by a band of robbers. They beat the poor traveller, who was alone. They stripped the clothes off him, and robbed him of everything of value. So severely was he beaten, that he was left for dead, lying on the ground.

It so happened that a Priest from the Temple was passing down the same road. He saw the poor wounded traveller lying on the ground. Instead of doing anything to help him, even though he was a Jew, the Priest just passed by on the other side of the road. Some time after that, a Levite, (perhaps a member of the Jewish choir), also passed by the beaten traveller. The Levite saw the man lying on the ground. Yet, he also did nothing to help. He just passed by on the other side of the road.

Some time passed, and the donkey came down the road, carrying the Samaritan. When he reached the wounded traveller, the good Samaritan stopped. He dismounted, and came to have a closer look. He took pity on the poor man because of the terrible injuries he had received. This he did, despite the fact that the traveller was of a different religion. He treated the traveller very kindly. Tending his wounds with care, he used both oil and wine to relieve them, just as we might put ointment or antiseptic on our wounds. After bandaging the man's injured limbs, the Samaritan then gently placed the Jewish traveller on his donkey.

The good Samaritan walked by the side of his donkey, supporting the wounded man. He brought him to an way-side inn, where he nursed him all night long. The next day, he gave the Inn-keeper a sum of money, and told him to take care of the wounded traveller. The Samaritan said, "If his bill comes to more than I am giving you now, then I will pay the extra, the next time I come." The good Samaritan went off down the road on his donkey.

Jesus told this story to explain matters to a lawyer, who asked, "Who is my neighbour." The story means that anyone who is in need of help is our neighbour. We should be a friend to everyone, no matter what their race or religion.

Prayer:

> Lord we thank you for the parables of Jesus.
> Make us like the Good Samaritan.
> May we be friendly to everyone,
> in our school, and not just to a few.
> Make us generous, and kind.
> Help us to show a good example.   Amen.

Hymn:

Teachers' Note: (1) Religion should not make us dislike any person. (2) The Good Samaritan's kind action, reminds us that people of other religions also may be genuinely good people. (3) To help someone else will cost us something.

(a) The Farmyard Bully   *Week 6   Bullying*

At the foot of the Rocky Mountains in Canada, there was a farm. It was simply a large log cabin, with fields behind it, going up to the edge of the mountain forest. The actual farm-yard was an area of ground, surrounded by a fence of cut Pine timber. Inside the timber fence the hens, geese, ducks and turkeys wandered about quite freely.

Now, if ever there was a bully, it was Mr. Turkey-Gobbler, the biggest turkey on the farm. He had large grey feathers, a red head, and a black beak. His legs and claws were yellow. He used his large beak to peck at any bird that happened to be near him. He was a very proud turkey. When he became thoroughly bad-tempered, his head became very red and flushed indeed, just as if it was going to burst with anger. He made a loud gobbling sound, and for this reason the farmer called him Mr. Turkey Gobbler.

None of the farm animals liked him. He would strut about the farm, pecking at the hens and their little chickens. He would chase the ducks into the duck pond. He would even try to frighten the grey geese. The geese all stood together, stretched out their necks, and made hissing sounds at him. Mr. Turkey-Gobbler would kick out at Flossie, the sheep dog. She would snarl back. He would even run at human beings and try to peck them. He was a bully all of the time. He was a horrible turkey!

One day he went into the milk-shed and pecked the milk-maid. She was so frightened that she over-turned the milk churn. The milk and the butter spilled all over the floor. Flossie the sheep-dog lapped up the milk, and ate up the butter. When the farmer called Flossie, she could not come. The farmer went for firewood, and he slipped and fell into a bed of stinging nettles. The turkey's bad behaviour seemed to be affecting everyone on the farm. Everyone was becoming disgusted with Mr. Turkey Gobbler the Farm-Yard Bully.

One very hot day, the big turkey saw what appeared to be a dog climbing through a hole in the Pine fence. The animal lay down in a crouching position as if it were asleep, with its eyes half shut. Mr. Turkey-Gobbler thought to himself, I will go over there and torment that sleeping dog. He did not realise that the crouching animal was not a dog, but a fierce and hungry Wolf. Just as the turkey stretched out his head to give the animal a nasty peck, the Wolf opened his eyes, and snapped with his teeth. He caught the turkey in his mouth, pulled it through the hole in the fence, and ran away with Mr. Turkey-Gobbler in his jaws.

The farmer was out-side the fence near the edge of the forest, with his gun on his arm. He saw what had happened. He aimed his gun, and shot the Wolf. He carried the frightened turkey under his arm, and put it safely back into the farmyard. Soon afterwards,the farm yard fowl and animals noticed that Mr. Turkey-Gobbler had changed his ways. He still pecked others sometimes, but not as often as before. Maybe, he was trying to be good!

Now, let us think about our own school. Sometimes a bully appears in a school. It may be either a girl or a boy. They did not mean to become a bully, but the bad habit of hurting other children slowly grew on them. A bully is an unhappy person, who tries to take it out on other people. He or she can make other children very unhappy. No one likes a bully. One thing is sure, a bully is heading for trouble in the future. Bullies end up by hurting themselves. We ought to do unto others, as we would have others do unto us. It always is better to make a friend than to make an an an enemy.

Prayer:

> O Lord, help us not to be over-bearing and rude.
> Teach us not to oppress any other person,
> either by what we say, or by what we do.
> Rather, help us to be friendly and understanding,
> to all our school-friends, and our Teachers.
> Show us how to make peace, and keep peace,
> within our school, and within ourselves.   Amen.

Hymn:

> All the animals. (C&P.2 80)

Teachers' Note: (1) Mr. Turkey-Gobbler could have been admired by the farm-yard fowl and animals. He was such a splendid bird. (2) It is not enough to be beautiful and strong in outer appearance. We must also aim to have a strong and beautiful inward character. (3) Pride comes before a fall.

(b) The King who was a Bully   *Week 6   Bullying*

When a King is a bully, he can cause so much suffering to ordinary people. We are going to consider some of the bad things King John did, and then the very important good that came out of it all. King John has the reputation of being the worst King that England ever had. He was said by some historians to have been a cruel ruler, and a man that no-one could ever trust.

First, he tried to keep his brother in prison.

For a long time, John was not really the King of England. It was his brother Richard the Lion Heart who was the crowned King of England. Richard ruled for ten years, (1189-1199), but he only spent seven months in his kingdom. Richard was away at the wars, with an army in the Crusades, fighting for the recovery of Jerusalem.

He had appointed John, his younger brother, to look after England for him, until he returned. John heard that King Richard on his return journey to England, had been put in prison by the Emperor of Germany. The Emperor wanted a ransom of one hundred thousand pounds paid to him, before he would let Richard go free. John was pleased. He thought, "Now I can become King of England myself". He wrote a letter to the Emperor, asking him to keep Richard imprisoned.

However, the people of England collected the money, and paid the ransom, and the good King Richard was set free. When Richard met John again in England, John pretended to be sorry for his bad conduct. Richard forgave him for all his bad behaviour. A short time after, good King Richard died.

Secondly. John killed his little nephew.

John had an older brother, called Geoffrey who previously had died. Geoffrey left a son, called Arthur, who was only twelve years old. He had a better claim to be King, than John had. John captured the boy Arthur, put him into a dungeon, and finally killed him. Everybody in England was shocked at such a terrible deed, by an uncle on his little nephew.

Thirdly, John made people pay heavy taxes.

John was always asking for money. In those days ordinary people were desperately poor. Ordinary people looked to the local Nobleman, or the Knight in his castle to protect them. The poor people in return for protection served their leader in the castle. King John made the Nobles raise money from the poor people by increased taxes. Two thousand Nobles and Knights of England, in order to protect themselves, and ordinary people, from the bully King, armed themselves. Their soldiers united together to force King John to sign the Magna Carta. (This means the "Great Charter" in the Latin language.) King John signed the Magna Carta at Runnymeade in the year 1215.

Some time after that, King John refused to keep the agreement he had signed. He brought foreign soldiers into England. His army was crossing the sands at the "Wash" when the rising tide rushed back, and all his baggage waggons went under the sea. Worse still, he lost the crown Jewels under the waves. Even the money to pay the foreign soldiers was lost in the water. The foreign soldiers went home. King John, the bully King, fell ill, and died at Newark, in poverty. Many people think that someone may have poisoned him, because everyone hated him so much. The Nobles and common people thought of John as being an evil man.

Something very good came out of the it all! In the Magna Carta, there is one clause in chapter 39 which reads, "No freeman shall be taken or imprisoned, except by the lawful judgement of his peers, or by the law of the land." Kings who were bullies were not allowed in England any more. Even the King had to submit to the rule of English law. It was established for all time, that Kings had not the power to put anyone into prison, or take away their property, without permission of the law. This is why we have Juries of twelve people in our Courts today. Judges hear the evidence in court, but it is the Jury who decides who is guilty, or not guilty.

Prayer:

> O Father God, make us all thankful for our rights,
> in the eyes of the law of the land.
> We thank you that every man, woman, boy and girl,
> is important in the eyes of Government.
> We thank you for wise Judges, and sensible Juries.
> Teach us, young and old, justice and fairplay.   Amen.

Hymn:

> When a knight won his spurs. (C&P.l. 50)

Teachers' Notes: (1) King John could have been a good King, but he was a bully by nature. (2) One deliberately bad act, is usually followed by many more bad deeds. John was full of treachery. (3) Even bad people cannot stop good happening. In the long run, good is always stronger than evil. The knowledge of the Magna Carta has brought justice to many nations of the world.

94

(c) A Soldier Bully

There is a story in the Bible about a soldier, named Goliath who was really a bully. David's brothers were Israelite soldiers in King Saul's army. The Israelite army was fighting the Philistine army. The two armies were camped facing each other, with a valley in between. Saul was the King of the Israelites. The Bible says that he was a man who was head and shoulders above all the people. King Saul therefore was a very tall man. David, as the King's musician, had previously played the harp before King Saul, to calm Saul's nerves, when the king had been depressed. On this occasion, however, David had been sent by his father to the battle field, to carry food to his soldier brothers, and to bring back news about them.

When David was visiting the Israelite camp, he looked across the valley. The giant of a man, named Goliath, appeared. He was three metres tall. He wore a bronze helmet, a coat of heavy iron mail, and he wore bronze leggings. In his hand he carried a large bronze and iron javelin. Goliath had an armour-bearer walking in front of him carrying his huge shield.

The young lad David watched as Goliath challenged the Israelite army. He shouted, "We do not need a war to settle our differences. Choose someone to represent your army, and I will fight him. If your champion kills me , then we will become your slaves. If I kill your champion, then you must be our slaves. I defy the whole army of Israel. Send out a man who will fight me." Goliath, twice every day, morning and evening, for forty days, made his challenge. No-one was willing to fight him.

When King Saul heard this, even though he was a tall man, he also was afraid. Indeed, all the Israelite soldiers were afraid of Goliath. When the young lad David heard Goliath taunting the Israelite soldiers, he asked, "Who is this man who defies the army of the living God". David's oldest brother, who was a soldier, said to David, "Where are your sheep, you are supposed to be looking after? You are a conceited young lad. You have only come here to find out how the battle is going. Mind your own business!".

David said to other soldiers, "I will fight this Philistine." King Saul heard of this and sent for David. He said to David, "You cannot fight Goliath. You are only a boy, and this man has been a fighting-man all his life." David answered. "when I was caring for my father's sheep, and a lion or a bear came and carried off a sheep, I went after it and rescued the sheep from its mouth. If it attacked me, then I used my club to kill it. I have killed both a lion and a bear. The Lord who saved me from the lion and the bear will save me from this Philistine."

Saul agreed that David should fight Goliath. He dressed David in his own suit of armour. David said, "I have never worn such armour before. I do not want to wear it." Instead, David took his staff in his hand, and he chose five smooth stones from the stream. He put the stones in his shepherd's bag. Then he took his sling, and went out to face the Philistine.

Goliath could not believe his eyes. A shepherd boy was standing before him, challenging him to a fight. "Am I a dog, that you come before me with sticks? Come and I will give your flesh to the birds of the air," he said. David answered, "You come against me with a sword, a spear, and a javelin, but I come against you, in the name of the Lord Almighty, the God of the armies of Israel. Today, the Lord will hand you over to me."

As Goliath moved forward to fight, David took a stone out of his shepherd's bag. He put the stone into his sling, and slung it at Goliath. The stone struck Goliath on the forehead. Goliath fell face downwards to the ground. David ran forward, and pulled out Goliath's sword, and killed Goliath with it. When the Philistine army saw that their champion was dead, they turned and ran away.

Goliath was another kind of bully. He met his match in fighting David the shepherd boy. David was later to become the king of Israel, after Saul had been killed in battle. David was very brave to face a giant of a man, such as Goliath.

Prayer:

>Lord help us to be brave like David.
>Give us a faith and a courage,
>when evil appears to us like a strong enemy.
>Help us to see that good is stronger than evil,
>and truth is stronger than falsehood.
>Make us to understand, if God is for us,
>then no-one can be against us.   Amen.

Hymn:

>O Lord, all the world belongs to you. (C&P.1 39)

Teachers' Note: The story is found in I Samuel Ch. 17. (1) David was quite young. Young people may have a strong faith in God. (2) David was an example to older people. (3) David showed early signs of leadership.

(a) Using our Time to Reach Goals

There was once a mountain hare who was very proud of his ability to run at speed. Indeed, he could also jump over a hedge if the hunting hounds were chasing him. He was a vain and boastful hare. The tortoise happened to be walking slowly down the road, when the hare caught up with him in a few leaps. "Hullo, tortoise", he said. "Your legs are very short, and you walk very slowly. Look at my legs, I have two long legs at the back, and two short legs at the front. They help me to run, and also to take long leaps when I need to. Let us have a race, and we'll run to the next mile stone."

To the hare's surprise, the tortoise accepted the challenge. "Yes, I am willing to run in a race with you to the next milestone," he said. The tortoise was really a good sport! Off they both went, starting from the big oak tree. The hare ran round the first bend of the road, and then round the second bend. It was a very hot day. He stopped and looked back. He knew that he had left the tortoise far behind.

"I'll just stop here, and enjoy a little sleep. I can waken up, after ten minutes, and run the race again. There will be plenty of time to reach the milestone, before the tortoise." So the hare curled up and went to sleep, lying by the side of the road. The tortoise could not move his legs any faster, so he just plodded slowly down the road. It took him a long time, but he at last reached the place where the hare was lying. By this time the hare was snoring in a deep sleep.

The tortoise did not stop, but just kept walking in his slow and determined manner. On, and on, and on, his little legs carried him, until after what seemed to be a long time he reached the milestone down the road. Almost exhausted, the tortoise lay down on the grass. After a while, the hare opened his eyes, and he remembered that he was running in a race. Off he bounded, and leaped, and soon reached the milestone. He was very surprised to see that the tortoise had reached the milestone before him. All the other animals and birds who were watching the race, agreed that the tortoise was the winner!

The mistake which the hare had made, was that he knew that he had plenty of time, to win the race, so he just wasted it in sleep. No one could ever say that the hare had put his best into the race. He showed himself to be a lazy hare. On the other-hand, the tortoise kept walking, and did not waste any time. He just plodded on. He never stopped until he had reached his goal.

We all have the same amount of hours in a day. Some people use up the time to their advantage in life, and do not give up, until they reach their goals. Many other people who have superior talents and skills, become conceited and careless. They give up too easily. Some others just waste their time. This means that often the ordinary pupils, can surpass the clever pupils, if they work harder. It is how you use your time that counts.

Prayer:

>Lord, show us that each of us has a talent.
>May we practice what we are good at,
>to improve ourselves.
>Teach us that girls and boys,
>may achieve their goals,
>by hard work, and careful preparation.
>Help us not to give up the race too early.   Amen.

Hymn:

>I planted a seed. (C&P.2. 134)

Teachers' Note: (1) Some people are more skilled than others. We have to learn to accept ourselves for what we are. The hare was a hare, and the tortoise was a tortoise. That could not be changed. (2) The better gifted people do not always reach their goals in life, because they may be lazy and waste their time. (The hare slept.) (3) Often it is the ordinary person who knows how to persist in what has to be done, who wins through. (The tortoise used his time to keep going, and he never gave up.)

(b) Ronnie's Secret

Week 7   Time

Ronnie was a good lad, but he seemed to have one bad habit. He was always late. At night he went to bed very late, after watching television. Next morning when he came to school, despite being warned about it by his teacher, he was often late. He would yawn in class. When he went home again, his Mum would be worried, because he reached home later than anyone else. He was a good footballer, but the trouble was that the match had begun, when Ronnie arrived late carrying his football boots.

He was to act the part of one of the Seven Dwarfs in the school Pantomime, "Snow White," but only six Dwarfs came on the stage on the first night of the show. Ronnie arrived at the Pantomime at half-past-seven, when he should have been there for seven o'clock. Everyone knew that when the children were going by coach to the seaside, that they would have to make sure that Ronnie was there on time. One of the Teachers would take him by the hand, and make sure that he was on the coach. When Ronnie went to church on Sunday, he would arrive as the second hymn was being sung. He was even late for his meals at home. Ronnie's Dad and Mum worried about him. For some unknown reason, Ronnie was different from the other children.

Ronnie had a secret, which he never revealed to anyone at home, or in the school. Ronnie had been ill for six weeks, just at the point when his teacher had taught the children in class to tell the time. The teacher was very proud that the children had learnt to tell the time so quickly. Ronnie came back to school after six weeks in the hospital. He never told anyone his secret. He could not tell the time! On his eighth birthday, Dad bought Ronnie a wrist watch. It was not the digital kind of watch, but a watch with two hands on it.

Ronnie loved his watch, but it was not of any use to him. What could he do now? Everyone would find out his secret, and laugh at him. They might even shout at him, "Stupid Ronnie cannot tell the time!" He knew the numbers round the face alright, but he could not understand the meaning of the two hands.

His teacher admired the new watch on Ronnie's wrist. Ronnie blushed red as a beetroot. His teacher noticed that the watch was set to half past six, when the real time was ten o'clock in the morning. At once his teacher understood Ronnie's problem. She set the class some work to do, and then she called Ronnie outside the class-room. "Have you a secret to share with me, Ronnie?" she asked. Ronnie, hesitated, and then he said, "I cannot tell the time! I was ill, and away from school, when the other children learnt about it," Ronnie said.

The teacher thought for a little moment. Then she said, "Ronnie, let us both keep a little secret together. We will not tell anyone in the class. Tomorrow, I am going to teach the children all about the clock again. I want you to bring your new watch with you. I'll set the children a project about "clocks", and I will also teach you specially how to read your watch and tell the time. If we do it that way, then no-one will ever know our secret."

So next day, in class, everyone was writing about clocks, or doing sums about time. Even in the art lesson, they used crayons and paints to make pictures of clocks and watches. The Teacher used every spare moment she could find to teach Ronnie about the Hour hand and the Minute hand. She taught him how to tell the time. In a couple of days, without any of the children knowing about it, Ronnie could look at his watch, and tell the time.

The children were surprised that Ronnie was never late at school again. Only his teacher knew about Ronnie's old secret. Teacher used to smile and say to Ronnie, sometimes, "Ronnie, I have left my watch at home, tell me the right time?" Ronnie always smiled back, when he told her the time exactly.

Sometimes children at school have secrets which are really little worries. It is also good for children to tell their parents, or their teacher about it. A secret shared with someone you trust takes away all the worry. It is good to be prompt. People say, "Better late than never! Better never late!" Do you know what that means?

Prayer:

> Lord, we thank you for the gift of time.
> Teach us to be prompt.
> Teach us not to waste our time.
> Help us to be the kind of friends,
> with whom others could share their worries.
> May we always bring our fears to God.   Amen.

Hymn:

> Time is a thing. (C&P.2. 104)

Teacher's Note: (1) It is always a good thing to try to be on time. (2) Secret worries are better shared with someone we trust. (3) Bad habits can be broken. (Ronnie never was late again.)

(c) Time and Generosity   *Week 7   Time*

Jesus told a parable about an employer, who owned a vineyard. He owned fields of vine trees which produced juicy grapes. The grape harvest ripened in September. Immediately after that, the rains came. Sometimes gathering in the harvest of grapes, had to be done quickly, before the rains fell. Employers would employ extra workers, even for a few hours.

The employer went out early one morning, and he hired men to work for him in his vineyard. He agreed to pay them one denarius for a day's work. (This was Roman money.)

A few hours later, the employer saw more men standing in the market place doing nothing. He told them to go and work in his vineyard, and at the end of the day, he would pay them the right wage. At twelve o'clock the employer hired several more men to work for him. At three o'clock he saw more men standing, so he also hired them to work. Then at five o'clock in the evening, he saw yet more men standing. He also hired them to work for him.

That evening, he told his manager to call the men, and to pay them their wages, beginning with the men who came last. These workers received one denarius each, which was one day's wages. Then when the men came who were hired earlier, he also paid them, one denarius. They all received the same wage. The men who had worked longer hours protested to the employer.

You have only paid us one denarius, and we have worked all day in the heat of the sun. Yet you have paid these men who have worked less hours, the same wage as we have received. The employer answered," I did you no wrong. I paid you what we agreed was the right wage. Take your wages and go. I want to give the same wage to everyone because I am a kind man. There is no law against being kind. I can give away my money if I like."

There are many people who work long hours, but they love the work they are doing. If they get fair wages that is all they want. They are happy and contented people. They do not want to reduce anyone else's wages. This parable also means that there is nothing wrong with someone being generous to others.

When you give something away, of your own free will, you are being generous. Being generous is a kind of sharing. Have you ever given anything away? Many people think that the employer's action was unfair to his workers. It would only have been unfair, if any worker had received less that the wage agreed at the beginning. The story also shows the difference between something expected and earned, and something unexpected and received as gift. Everything that comes from God is a gift!

Prayer:

> Father, God, teach us to use up the hours at school,
> because learning is a kind of working.
> Show us how to be generous to others.
> May we be unselfish, and not be greedy.
> Grant that we may value our time,
> and spend it in a good manner.   Amen.

Hymn:

> God knows me. (C&P.l. 15)

Teacher's Note: This difficult Parable is found in St. Matthew Ch. 20. (1) Not everyone works the same number of hours. The deep sea fishermen may be away from home for weeks. (2) Everyone likes to be treated fairly, so we must treat others in a similar manner. (3) Being generous means giving to others, without even expecting thanks. (God's gifts can never be earned).

(a) Faith in a Leader
Week 8   Faith

Tony attended the local Comprehensive school. He went to Switzerland on a Winter holiday, with four other older boys and his school Teacher. They travelled by air to Bern airport. Part of the distance, they travelled by coach. They completed the remaining part of the journey by mountain railway. The group stayed in a hotel in a ski-ing resort, high in the Swiss Alps. The country-side and mountains were covered in a deep blanket of snow, because it had been snowing heavily during the previous week.

Tony had already practised ski-ing on a artificial ski slope in Lancashire. He had a rough idea of what to do. In a couple of days Tony and his school friends soon learnt to move over the snow downhill with a certain amount of skill. The Teacher encouraged them, by saying "Practice makes perfect."

On the fifth day of the holiday, the school group decided to join another group, and go for a mountain trail walk and climb. The trail had often been used by tourists on holiday. The Alpine Guide was a strong young man, who carried among other things, a spare rope wrapped over his shoulder, and fixed securely to his waist. He tied a rope which had a red line through-out its length, around each person's waist. There were eleven people in the group, and Tony was number nine.

Off they went, climbing slowly over the snow, in a long line of climbers. It was not a very steep path, nevertheless they were ascending higher and higher all the time. They went round bends ascending the wide trail. The Alps looked very beautiful that day, covered in pure white snow. The sky was a clear blue colour. They wore green-tinted glasses because the glare of the snow might damage their eyes. Tony and his friends were enjoying themselves.

Higher up, the trail narrowed into a rather winding path. After a time, the whole party stopped. Away ahead of the line, the Alpine guide, was helping each member of the group, one at a time, across a gap in the rocky path. When Tony reached the gap, he realised that this was really a chasm between two mountains. He looked down, and he could see the hotel and the valley down below. All at once, Tony became very nervous. He was so nervous and afraid, that he could not move his legs. He began to cry. Everyone was watching him. Those ahead of him dared not speak, and the two climbers behind him were also beginning to feel nervous.

The Alpine Guide, just smiled at Tony, and looked him straight in the eyes. Taking off his fur gloves, he said, "Tony, put your hands into my hands. Believe me! These hands have never let anyone fall yet!" Tony full of fear, put his hands into the strong hands of the Alpine Guide. "Now, Tony keep your eyes open, and take take one big step. I will catch and hold you." Tony felt the Guide's hands securely holding him. Tony stepped forward, and it was as if he had been lifted over the snowy chasm. The Alpine Guide said, "Good Lad! Well done!." He proceeded to help the other two members of the group step over the gap.

Nothing was said by anyone in the group, as the path again became wider, becoming a trail, which gently led round and down the snowy hill, and back to the hotel where they were staying. Tony and his friends had talked about the adventure, after it was past. The Alpine Guide sat down beside Tony and showed him what he always carried on his person when he was on duty. An extra rope; a large pen-knife with many tools on it; a first aid kit; a walkie-talkie radio; a torch; a small cannister of oxygen and a mask; a survival bag, and a flask of something hot to drink.

Tony felt rather foolish about his being afraid on the mountain path. The Alpine Guide smiled again at Tony and said, "Tony you have learnt one very important lesson today. On the mountain, you must always have faith in your Leader." Tony smiled back, and nodded his head.

Christians always have faith in their leader, Jesus. All religions have leaders, who have been holy people in their life-time. Our families have leaders in our Parents. In our Schools it is the Teachers who are our leaders.

Prayer:

> Lord, be our Leader!
> We thank you for the people who lead us,
> especially our parents, and our teachers.
> Help us to to trust those Leaders,
> whom we know will lead us,
> to do what is good, true, and sensible.
> May we never follow any Leader,
> who will lead us into doing wrong.   Amen.

Hymn:

> He's got the whole world. (C&P.l. 19)

Teachers' Note: (1). There is great value in attempting a difficulty together with others. (2) It is usual to need encouragement when we are fearful. (3) Especially in times of emergency, children should trust their Leader. Teachers can be trusted.

(b) Faith and Trust

Week 8   Faith

In the reign of Queen Victoria, there were many large houses owned by rich people. These gentry often employed a number of servants in their homes. In one manor house, a rich man and his wife needed a housemaid. They advertised in the local newspaper, and a young lady applied for the job. Her name was Charlotte, and she was a good Christian. She tried to do her work as well as she could, because she believed that if anyone had faith, then they must also have good actions. So she polished the furniture well, and swept the floors as carefully as she could. She was very well mannered, clean, and tidy. Charlotte needed a job, because she had to pay to look after her mother, who was a widow, and lived in another village. Charlotte's father had died when she was very young.

Charlotte arrived at the rich man's manor house. She rang the door bell, and was invited in to the house to meet the owners. She had gone to the front door this time, because this was a special occasion. In ordinary circumstances, she would have had to go into the house by the servant's entrance round the corner. The lady and gentleman gave Charlotte a long interview. They asked her many questions, because a housemaid in a private household would need to be a reliable person. After much questioning, Charlotte was employed as housemaid. She was told all her duties, which were written down on a sheet of paper. Charlotte lived in an upstairs attic, at the top of the house.

Charlotte was very happy at finding such a job. She polished the brass candlesticks with all her energy. The large carpets often had smaller rugs over them, to save the large carpet from too much wear. Charlotte lifted up the rugs and swept underneath them. She really tried to do her best for her employers.

After a few weeks, the lady and gentleman had a conversation with each other. The lady said, "How do we know that Charlotte really sweeps underneath the rugs? Maybe she only pretends to keep the place tidy. How do we really know that she is honest, and hard working? I think that we should set her a test in secret." The gentleman thought that this was a good idea. So they put a gold sovereign under one corner of the rug in the drawing room. "We will come back and see whether Charlotte really sweeps under the rugs, and if she is honest."

Next day the employers came down to the drawing room. and they looked under the corner of the rug. To their dismay, the gold sovereign was missing. The lady said to the gentleman, "There, I always knew that housemaids were dishonest. Probably she has not swept underneath the rug either." The lady pulled the bell rope to call the housemaid to the drawing room. Charlotte arrived immediately. "Yes, Madam, you called me," she said. The lady and gentleman were very angry. They said, "We secretly tested you yesterday, to see if you were a good worker, and whether you were honest or not. We put a gold sovereign under this carpet, and it is missing. You must have stolen it."

Charlotte was shocked, by this lack of trust in her. However, she smiled at the her employers, and sweetly said, "No Madam, your gold sovereign has not been stolen. If you look under the other corner of your rug, you will find it there!" The lady and gentleman rushed over to the other corner, and looked underneath. Sure enough, there was the gold sovereign!

"Charlotte said, "I found your gold coin under the rug yesterday, when I was sweeping underneath it. I decided that as you were testing me, then I would test you! I put the gold sovereign under the other corner to test whether you trusted me or not! It seems that you do not trust a housemaid who is trying her best to be good and honest. I believe in God, so I do not steal." The lady and the gentleman were very ashamed of themselves, because they had mis-trusted Charlotte.

Charlotte said to her employers, "I forgive you both." From that day onwards, her employers knew that she would always be trustworthy.

Prayer:

> Lord God, give us a strong faith in you.
> Show us that faith produces good actions.
> May we always be young people,
> who can be trusted by others,
> to do what is right, honest, and kind.
> Forgive us if we have ever been unworthy of trust.   Amen.

Hymn:

> God has promised. (C&P.l. 31)

Teachers' Note: (1) Faith is believing in God. No matter what job we do, we need faith. (2) If we have faith, then our actions will be good. You cannot have faith and always be doing evil things. (3) Faith in God makes us trust-worthy people.

(c) A Slave Healed by Faith   *Week 8   Faith*

In the Roman army there were regiments, called "Legions," made-up at different times of, three thousand to six thousand soldiers. These legions were divided up into companies of one hundred soldiers each, called "Centuries." The officer in charge of the hundred soldiers was called a "Centurion." When Jesus was alive, his land was part of the Roman Empire. The Roman soldiers kept law and order in the towns and villages under the local command of the Roman Centurion.

A Roman officer had a slave who had fallen very ill and who was lying at home paralysed. (Slaves were unpaid servants. Slaves were a class of people who did not own anything. They often were people captured in war. They could be bought from, or sold to another person.)

Usually slaves were not counted to be of much importance. Their masters often beat them, and no-one bothered whether the slave lived or died. No-one cared for them. Sometimes a good slave would have a kind Master, or Mistress. Both people would become good friends. This is apparently what had happened here, because the Centurion certainly cared for his slave.

The Roman Centurion had a difficult problem to face. Jesus was a Jew. He being a Roman soldier was a Gentile. (not a Jew). According to the Jewish religion, Jews were not allowed to enter into the house of a Gentile. Non-Jews were said to be religiously unclean.

The Centurion said to Jesus, "Lord, I do not deserve that you should come under my roof. If you just say the word, I know that my slave will be healed. Again, the Centurion spoke to Jesus, saying, "In one way I am a like you. I am a man under authority. My superior officer in command gives me orders, and I in turn give orders to my soldiers and slaves. I say to them, 'go, or come' and they obey me. Lord you have only to say the word of healing, and my sick slave will get better."

This meant that the Roman Centurion believed that if Jesus wanted, he had the power to make the slave well again. Jesus said, "I have not met anyone in the land with such great faith as you have. Go home, and it shall be done just as you believed it would." When the Roman Centurion reached home, he found, that his slave had been healed. The story shows that Jesus had the power to heal even without meeting the sick person.

Nowadays, when we are very ill, we are rushed off to a hospital. The fact that we are rushed off to hospital means that we must have some kind of faith in the Doctors and Nurses. They have much knowledge, and great skills in healing people. Yet the strange thing is that Doctors and Nurses will always say that they do not heal anyone. They just perform the operations, and take care of the wounds, and administer the medicines. Christians believe that it is God who has so designed the human body, that after the Doctors' operation and care, the body heals itself. We need to have faith in God, faith in the Doctors, faith in medicines, and faith in our own bodies, if we are to be healed. Faith means to "Trust."

Prayer:

> Father God, we thank you for our bodies;
> they are wonderfully made.
> Teach us to care for our bodies,
> by living sensibly, and by eating a healthy diet.
> We thank you for Doctors and Nurses;
> for hospitals, medicines, and operations.   Amen.

Hymn:

> A man for all the people. (C&P.1. 27)

Teachers' Note: (1) As far as we know, the Centurion was not a Christian, nor was he a Jew. Yet Jesus was interested in him. God loves people of all races and religions. (2) The Centurion came to the right person for healing. Jesus sent him home happy. Many people know what it is to go to hospital for healing, and to go home better. (3) Faith in God helps the body to heal. Prayer is a form of asking for healing.

(a) A Land of Hope

In the seventeenth century, there were a large number of Christian people in England known as "Puritans." They were very religious people, and loved to read the Bible. They believed that everyone in the Church should have a personal faith in God. When the King had a dis-agreement with Parliament, Puritans usually supported Parliament rather than the King. They earned everyone's respect, because they were good workers.

The Puritans preferred to worship God in a very simple manner, without images, candles, or clergy being dressed in splendid robes. Archbishop Laud, who was then Archbishop of Canterbury, persecuted these Puritan Christians so much, that they felt that they had to leave England. They had hoped to sail to North America, to find a country where they would be free to worship God according to their own consciences. For them, America was a land of hope.

Previously, in 1620, other Puritans who became known as the, "Pilgrim Fathers" had set sail from Plymouth, in a famous wooden sailing ship called the "Mayflower". This ship was very small. It was only 30 metres long, and 6 metres wide. The passengers lived below deck in a space little more than one metre high. There were no port-holes. Oil lamps were necessary below deck. The voyage across the Atlantic Ocean took about one hundred days to accomplish. Often men, women, and children were sea-sick for days on end, as they lay below deck. The Mayflower sailed speedily over the rough waves, blown by the wind.

The Pilgrim Fathers had hoped to reach North America after sailing across the Atlantic Ocean, to the British colonies. Other brave British people had gone before them. Thirteen British colonies eventually were established along the coast. After a dangerous voyage, the Mayflower carrying about one hundred new settlers and their families reached America, on December 15th. 1620. They disembarked at Cape Cod, in Massachusetts. The area became known as "New England". Years later a million more people from England were to follow them.

The Puritan settlers' families were unprepared for the very cold American Winter. They had to build themselves log cabins in which to live. During that first year nearly one half of the settlers died, because of sickness, or because of the freezing cold. The remaining settlers waited with great hope, until the Spring came. The local Indians showed them how to grow maize. This meant that when harvest time came round, they had enough maize to keep as next year's seed. They also had enough maize to crush in the mill, to make flour. From the flour they could make bread to eat through the Winter months. From then onwards the settlers usually had sufficient food to eat.

When Harvest time came round again, they held their first "Harvest Supper". Near the end of November, they were so happy that they kept one special day, and called it "Thanksgiving Day." They killed turkeys and geese, and cooked them to make a special Thanksgiving Day meal. They invited the Indians, who had helped them grow crops, to share the celebrations. Even in these modern times, the Americans still keep "Thanksgiving day." On that day they still eat turkey, sweet potatoes, cranberry sauce, and pumpkin pie.

The Pilgrim Fathers had hoped for a new and free way of life. They found it in America. America for them was a "Land of Hope." Many persecuted people, with their families later followed the Pilgrim Fathers across the ocean to "The New World".

In the year 1845-1846 a disease called the "potato blight" destroyed most of the potato crops which were growing in the fields of Ireland. Thousands of people starved to death. History repeated itself. Another stream of people known as "emigrants," and numbering one and a half million, sailed to America. They also found it a Land of Hope!

Prayer:

> O God our Father, when we pray to you,
> we always find new hope.
> When life is difficult for us,
> help us to understand
> that things always seem worse before they get better.
> Lord, may we never lose hope.   Amen.

Hymn:

> Lord of all hopefulness. (C&P.l. 52)

Teachers' Note: (1) Everyone has difficult times in life. Life sometimes seems unfair. (2) If we pray to God, he will give us all new hope. (3) Everyone needs a sure hope to keep going on. Hope is like someone waiting in the darkness for the morning light. Morning has never failed to come yet. Things will change for the better.

(b) The Song of Hope
Week 9   Hope

During the second World War, enemy aeroplanes would often come over the towns and cities of Britain to drop bombs on the factories. It became too dangerous for children to remain in a city. For reasons of safety, the children were evacuated to safer places in the country areas.

Five little boys became evacuees, and they were sent to live on a farm, seventy miles away from their own home city. They soon learned the names of the farm animals. The other children, who were brought up in the country, taught the city children the names of the wayside flowers, and the different kinds of trees. One day an exhausted Song Thrush flew into a large hen shed. The boys caught the bird, and made a cage for it, from an old apple-box. They covered the front of the box with chicken wire. They made a little door at the side of the box, to enable them to put food and water into the cage.

They were very interested in the Song Thrush, and very kind to it. The captured bird became well and strong again. However, the Song Thrush would not sing for the boys, even though they fed it with seed and nuts, They took care to keep fresh water in the cage. After about a week, they decided to clean out the cage. One of the boys opened the small door. As quickly as anyone could wink, the bird flew though the opening in the box. It flew around inside the hen shed once. Then it flew out through the big door. It was soon at the top of a high hedge, where no-one could reach it.

Then to the five boys surprise, the Song Thrush began to sing the sweetest and loudest song they had ever heard a bird sing. The five boys understood at last! The bird in the home-made cage would not sing, because its hope of freedom was gone. It had been a prisoner! The Song Thrush now on the hedge top had hope and freedom. It wanted to sing and tell everyone in the world! "I'm free. I am happy. I have hope".

Have you ever heard the loud sweet song of the Thrush on a Summer evening? Have you ever heard the "Dawn Chorus?" Birds wake up from sleep very early in the morning and break into song.

Oliver Herford (1863-1935) wrote these words.

> I heard a bird sing
> In the dark of December;
> A magnificent thing
> And sweet to remember;
> "We are nearer to Spring
> Than we were in September"
> I heard a bird sing
> In the dark of December.

Prayer:

> Heavenly Father, we thank you for the birds,
> that sing so sweetly in our hedges.
> Grant that we too may be like them,
> singing from our hearts.
> Bless everyone in our Assembly,
> and give new hope to each of us here.   Amen.

Hymn:

God knows me. (C&P.l. 15)

Teachers' Note: (1) It is not always easy to sing if you are worried about something. (2) Sometimes hope makes us sing, and sometimes when we sing it gives us hope. People in danger sometimes sing together. (3) Looking at the birds, and other creatures in nature, can teach us to be hopeful. Jesus taught that God cares for birds, and cares for us. Matthew Ch. 6. verses 26-27.

(c) Bringing New Hope   *Week 9   Hope*

One day Jesus was speaking to the people, when a Ruler of the Synagogue came to him. The Synagogue was the Jewish Church, where people met to hear the scriptures being read every Sabbath day. The Ruler's name was Jairus. He knelt at the feet of Jesus, in a very distressed state of mind. He begged Jesus to help him. Jairus told Jesus that his little girl, aged twelve years, was dying. "Come, Jesus and lay your hands on her, that she may be healed," he said. Jesus immediately set out for the House of Jairus, with a crowd of people following him.

As they made their way, there was a sick woman in the crowd. For twelve years, she had spent all her money, paying Doctor's bills, hoping to be cured. However, none of the Doctors could cure her. The sick woman thought to herself, "If I could only touch Jesus' clothes I might be cured." As the crowd gathered around Jesus, the sick woman stretched out her hand and touched the hem of Jesus' clothing. Immediately, she felt a new power pass through her body. She knew that she had been healed.

Jesus felt the healing power going out of him. He said, "Who touched me?" The Disciples replied, "Why are you asking who touched you? You are surrounded by a crowd, and everyone is touching you." The woman was afraid, and came forward. She knelt down before Jesus, and told him what had happened. Jesus said to her, "Daughter, your faith has healed you. Go in peace."

Just at that moment, people came from Jairus' house to say that the little girl had just died. "Do not trouble Jesus, the Teacher, any more," they said." Jesus heard them, and he said, "Don't be afraid, only have faith." Jesus took three of his disciples with him; Peter, James and John. By the time they had reached the Ruler's house, there was a loud commotion. People were weeping and wailing, and making a great noise, because Jairus' daughter had died. Jesus said to them, "The child is not dead, she is only asleep". When the people heard him say these words, they laughed at Jesus.

Then Jesus sent all the people out of the house. He brought the girl's parents, and his three disciples, into the room where the little girl was lying on the low bed. He took the girl by the hand, and said to her, "Get up, my child." The little girl opened her eyes, arose, and walked around the room. Jesus had made her well again. Everyone was amazed at the healing power of Jesus. He warned them that they should not let anyone know about what had happened. Jesus remembered that the girl might be hungry, so he told her Parents to prepare a good meal for her. Then Jesus moved on to another place.

Can you remember that the number twelve was mentioned twice in this story.? (The girl's age; The woman's sickness lasted twelve years.) Jairus probably had lost hope, when the news came through that his daughter had just died. The sick woman probably had lost hope of ever being cured, after paying Doctor's bills for such a long time. Jesus that day brought new hope to the girl's parents, and to the sick woman in the crowd.

Prayer:

Lord, show us that we must never lose hope.
Give us each one such a faith in God,
that hope will always be in our hearts.
Help us not to worry or fret.
Rather may we learn to be strong,
and by our inner strength,
may we encourage others to believe in God.   Amen.

Hymn:

Give us hope Lord. (C&P.2. 87)

Teachers' Note: The story is found in Matthew Ch.9, Mark Ch. 5., and Luke Ch. 8. (1) We ought to be thankful for health and strength. Anyone could fall sick at any age. (2) Jairus must have been a good man because he cared for the Synagogue, (Jewish Church). Yet his daughter was sick. It does not mean that you have done wrong because you happen to fall ill. (This is what people in Jesus' time believed) (3) Jesus brought hope to everyone in the story. The people believed the girl was dead, Jesus may have realised that the little girl was not dead, but in a coma. (an unconscious sleep). The healing is a miracle nevertheless.

(a) Pan-Cake Tuesday

Long ago, the Christian Church began to observe Lent as a period of fasting. Fasting means going without food. The meaning of the word, "Lent" is "Spring-time." Lent lasted through-out the six weeks period before Easter. It was a time for abstaining from certain kinds of food for religious reasons. Officially, Lent lasted forty days, beginning on Ash Wednesday. It also celebrated the experience of Jesus fasting forty days in the desert.

"Shrove Tuesday." was a day set aside by the church, so that people might confess their sins to God before Lent. Many of us know Shrove Tuesday better as "Pan-Cake Tuesday. This is because there grew up the custom of making pan-cakes on this day. No-one was supposed to eat rich food during the period of Lent. So rather than waste good food, people used up their eggs and butter, and made Pan-Cakes.

There were once seven Monks who lived in a small Monastery. They said their prayers together at certain fixed times. Each Monk had a special task to perform every day. One Monk kept the gardens. One looked after the animals and the poultry. Another Monk was the cook. Another Monk kept the fires burning in the large stone fire-places through-out the Monastery. This involved collecting the wood from the forest. One Monk served the food at meal time. One Monk read a Book aloud, when the others were eating in the refectory. They would change their duties around, from time to time. By this ordered way of doing things they found out which Monks were best certain tasks, such as cooking, or fishing, or looking after their two big dogs, Bruno and Barney. The Monk in charge of the Monastery was an Abbot called Brother Paul.

Brother Dennis was cook for the day. He remembered that it was "Pan-Cake Tuesday, so he made a batch of delicious Pan-Cakes for the evening meal. Brother Dennis thought, "How pleased, the other Brothers would be, when they sat down to eat at the long table that evening." Brother Francis was a hearty Monk who loved his food. He could not resist the appetising smell when he came past the kitchen. He popped his head through the kitchen door, and said to Brother Dennis, "I can hardly wait until the bell rings for my next meal. I am very hungry!" Brother Dennis just smiled at him.

The Monks worked hard at the task set for them that day. When the bell rang for the evening meal, they walked in a line into the Refectory, and took their places at the wooden table. They sat down on the benches, and Abbot Paul said the Grace before the meal. Suddenly, Brother Dennis, the cook, came rushing in to the Brothers. He said, "Someone has stolen the batch of Pan-Cakes. They are all gone!"

Brother John looked at Brother Peter. Brother Ignatius looked at Brother Silas. Brother Dennis looked at Brother Francis. The Abbot, Brother Paul looked at all of the Monks. The Monks began to feel most uncomfortable because of everyone else's searching looks. Brother Paul said, "This is Shrove Tuesday. If anyone confesses to stealing, and eating the Pan-Cakes, we will all forgive him." No-one said a word. No one owned up to taking the missing pan-Cakes.

Brother Francis sat smiling to himself. He looked so well-fed and healthy. Slowly everyone's eyes turned, and looked at him. They remembered that they had often heard Brother Francis talking about how he loved food. Then the Monks began to whisper to each other. Finally, Brother Silas stood up, and said to the Abbot, "We all feel sure that it was Brother Francis who has stolen the Pan-Cakes, and has eaten them up." Brother Paul being the Leader of the Community, and a very wise man, said, "We trust everyone in an equal manner here. If Brother Francis had eaten the Pan-Cakes he would have admitted it. A person is believed to be innocent until he has been proved guilty."

The other Brothers admitted that they had no evidence for accusing Brother Francis. The whole time, Brother Francis just smiled. He was a very good man. Then in a quiet voice he said, "I think that I know who has stolen the Pan-cakes." The Others asked, "Who is the thief?" Brother Francis said, "I think that you will find the thieves lying below the table. Someone forgot to feed them today." They looked underneath the long table, and saw Bruno and Barney lying asleep. Pan-Cake crumbs were lying on the stone floor, beside the dogs.

Immediately, the Monks realised just how wrong they had been in accusing Brother Francis. Slowly, Brother Francis said, "Since this is Shrove Tuesday, I will forgive all of you." The other monks were wiser men from that day forward. They never made false accusations against anyone again. Brother Francis, put his arms around Bruno and Barney. He loved animals. He whispered to the two dogs, "I'll forgive both you dogs as well!"

Prayer:

> Lord, we thank you for Shrove Tuesday.
> We thank you for Pan-Cake Tuesday.
> May we ask your forgiveness,
> when we have done wrong.
> Teach us never to make false accusations.
> Grant us the grace to forgive others.   Amen.

Hymn:

> Father, hear the prayer we offer. (C&P.l 48)

Teachers' Note: (1). Lent, the Spring Christian Festival, is a time for testing ourselves in the faith. (2). We all commit sins that God is willing to forgive. (3). A sin against our fellows, is a sin against God.

(b) A Surprise at Lent

There was an old school in a small village in the North of England. The school had a play-ground at the rear, and a green lawn at the front. The old Caretaker, Mr. Davies, was a Welsh-man. He and his family had left Wales to find work in England. Mr. Davies had been school Caretaker for thirty years. His family had now grown up. They had emigrated to Australia and found good jobs there. Mr. Davies and his wife remained in England. Mr. Davies had reached the age of 65 years. His family had written to their Dad and Mum to come out to Australia and retire there. The family had found a little house for them. Mr. and Mrs. Davies, after much thought, had decided to accept the invitation to leave England.

On the last day of Summer term, in July, all the pupils and Teachers met in the Worship Assembly. They presented Mr. and Mrs. Davies with a beautiful chiming clock, as a farewell present. The Headteacher and one pupil from each class made a little speech. They said how grateful they all were for Mr. Davies efficient ways of keeping the school and grounds so clean and tidy. They wished him and his wife every happiness in Australia.

Then Mr. Davies rose up to speak. There was a tear in his eye as he made his farewell speech. At the close of his speech, he said, "Now members of Staff, and children, this is the month of July. We shall fly to Australia in August. I want to tell you that just as you have given me this beautiful clock as a present, so I have decided to give this school a present. When you see it, I hope that you will remember me in my absence. Unfortunately, my present will not arrive until Lent next year. If you have patience to wait that long, then one day you will see my present arrive outside the school."

The children were mystified, and wondered what kind of a present Mr. Davies was going to give to the school. They knew that Lent usually began in March. Eight months seemed a long time for the school to wait for its present to arrive. Everyone shook hands and Mr. and Mrs. Davies went home.

Just a few weeks before the Davies left the village, a lorry called at their cottage. The lorry driver delivered three full sacks of what looked like onions. Every evening when the children and members of Staff had left school, Mr. Davies used to spend a little time tidying up the school front lawn. He always had a sack near him. Mr. and Mrs. Davies left the village and a new Caretaker began his duties. The children forgot about the Mr. Davies' promise.

The months passed. On a sunny March day the Headteacher said to the Worship Assembly. "Children, look, Mr. Davies' present has arrived. It is on the lawn in front of the school. I think that you will like it. We will ask all the children to line up, and go outside." When everyone came out to the front lawn, they were amazed to see that the lawn was completely covered with beautiful yellow daffodils.

Everyone realised that it was not onions which were in Mr. Davies's three sacks last July, but daffodil bulbs. Now everyone understood why they had to wait for such a long time for the present to arrive. The Headteacher told them that these bulbs which were planted under the grass, would come up every year. The children agreed that Lent was a lovely time to receive a present. They understood that Lent was another word for Spring-Time. All the children wrote letters to Australia, thanking Mr. and Mrs. Davies for the surprise gift.

Prayer:

> Lord, thank you for the gift of new life.
> Thank you for crocuses, and daffodils.
> Thank you for every hedge and tree,
> whose green leaves are beginning to appear.
> Thank you for Lent and Spring-time.
> We are grateful for the joys of nature,
> and the songs of birds at nesting time.   Amen.

Hymn:

> Lay my white cloak. (C&P.2. 112)

Teachers' Note: (1). Nature shows itself at Lenten time in new life. Just as Lent itself comes before Easter. (2). There is an annual rhythm in Nature, which Christians see as part of God's design. (Snowdrops, crocuses, daffodils, and tulips follow in order). (3) Daffodils, even when cut down, re-appear the following year. In Nature there is a dying and a rising again.

(c) Two People Put to the Test   *Week 10   Lent*

The season of Lent lasts for forty days. It has been connected with the testing of Jesus, because Jesus went without food for forty days. We all know that people may go without food for a long time. However, if we went without water for more than three days, then we would become very ill and die. Jesus had ended his lonely forty-day fast in the desert. Satan came to test Jesus, and to try to make him disobey God. At this moment, Jesus would be very weak, since he had not eaten food for such a long time. There were three tests. We should think of these tests as being in the mind of Jesus.

In the first test, Satan said to Jesus, "If you are the Son of God, then command that these stones be made into bread." Jesus replied to Satan, "It is written in the Scriptures, that man cannot live by bread alone, but by every word that comes from God." If Jesus had made stones into bread, then he would have been famous, and everyone might have liked him. He might have become a popular person. However, Jesus did not want to be famous for the wrong reasons. He did not want to be a magician.

Then Satan tested Jesus a second time. He took Jesus up to Jerusalem to the Jewish Temple. Jesus sat on a high pinnacle of the building. Satan suggested that Jesus should throw himself down from the high place. Satan argued that God would send angels to catch Jesus as he fell. He said that Jesus would not be hurt on the sharp rocks below. Jesus did not believe Satan's lies. Jesus said, "It is written that you must not tempt the Lord your God." This was another trick by Satan to try to spoil God's plan for Jesus.

Satan tested Jesus a third time. He took Jesus up a very high mountain. He showed him all the kingdoms of this world. Satan said, "I will give you all these kingdoms, if you will bow down and worship me." Jesus refused to bow down to Satan. Jesus said, "Go away, Satan! It is written in the Scriptures, You shall worship the Lord your God, and serve him alone." Satan left Jesus alone.

The reason Jesus did not take any notice of Satan in the third test, was that he did not come to rule a kingdom, as if he were a rich King. Instead, Jesus came to do God's will, and to help poor and sick people. Jesus showed that he had inner strength because he his stood ground during the three tests.

Children are tested sometimes to see if they will tell the truth. Wesley was an Irish boy with sandy coloured hair. He was nine years of age. He loved to play with a hammer and nails. One day, the other children watched him in his own back yard. He hammered a large six inch nail into a block of hard wood. Wesley had to hammer the nail for quite a time, before he could get the nail to go into the wood. Then Wesley tried to pull the big nail out of the wood again, but it would not come out. So he, forgetting where he was, held the heavy block by the nail, and threw it over his head, and over the yard wall. There was a loud sound of glass being smashed on the other side of the wall. The wooden block had gone through the window of the house in the next street.

When the man, whose window was broken, came running round to the next street to find the culprit, all the children ran away. No-one knew what had happened. Wesley was a very brave boy. He had been taught at home to be honest at all times. This was Wesley's testing time. Would he own up to the foolish deed which he had done, or would he deny it?

Wesley decided to tell the truth. He went up to the angry man and said, "I am sorry, I broke your window. I did not mean to do it. I'll give my pocket money to pay the Glazier to mend it. He will put a new pane of glass in your window for you. I am very sorry. It was very thoughtless of me to throw a block of wood over your yard wall."

The man was no longer angry. He looked at young Wesley, and shook him by the hand. "What an honest boy you are," he said. "Don't you tell your father when he comes home from work. Leave that part to me, and I will explain to him that it was all an accident." The Glazier came round immediately and repaired the window. And Wesley's father was very proud of his son. He had been tested, and he had told the truth. Lent is about the testing of Jesus, the man who never told a lie.

Prayer:

> Lord we thank you for the season of Lent.
> We are glad that Jesus stood the test.
> When we are tested to do wrong,
> give us strength to resist evil.
> May we use Lent to prepare our hearts,
> to celebrate Easter when it comes.   Amen.

Hymn:

> Dear Lord, and Father of mankind. (JP. 37)

Teachers' Note: This account of the Temptation is found in Matthew Chapter 4. (1) God allows us all to be tested at times. (2) Jesus was at his low point when tested by Satan. Testing seems to come to us at difficult moments in life. (3) Jesus knew his Scriptures. Knowing the Holy Bible, or the holy Scriptures of our religious tradition gives us inward strength.

(a) Saint David's Day   *Week 11   Three Saints Day*

There is not very much information in History about St. David the Patron Saint of Wales. March 1st. is kept as St. David's day. Welsh people wear leeks or daffodils on this day of celebration. It is thought that David was born about the year 520.A.D. He became a Priest in the Church of Wales. There was an island somewhere off the coast of Wales, and on it lived a very learned man called Paulinus the scribe. David spent ten years studying the Bible on the island with Paulinus as his teacher. Paulinus once went blind, perhaps, because he wrote and read too many books. David became famous, when he healed Paulinus, and gave him back his eyesight. David was different from other Priests, because he never would drink beer or wine. He drank only water. His food was bread, vegetables and salt. He was a splendid preacher and became Bishop of Menevia, (Welsh

Mynyw.) in the year 589 A.D. People loved him, because he encouraged so many churches to be built in Wales.

Here is a story for St. David's day. Gwyneth and Gareth were very good friends. Both of them were ten years old. Both lived in semi-detached houses, side by side, in a town in South Wales. Gareth had the misfortune to fall off his bicycle, and to fracture his leg in two places. He had to remain in hospital, with his leg in a plaster cast.

It was St. David's day, and Gwyneth decided to visit Gareth in hospital. She went up to the Glen, on the side of the mountain, and picked a bunch of wild daffodils to give to Gareth. The hospital, was rather a large one, situated in beautiful grounds. Gareth was pleased to see Gwyneth, but he did not seem to be pleased with the Daffodils. Gwyneth asked Gareth what was wrong.

Gareth said," Look at the hospital grounds! There are hundreds of daffodils growing around the lawns. Look at the vases of cut flowers in the wards! We have enough, without cutting wild daffodils! I think that we should take care of our environment. This means allowing Daffodils to grow in their natural surroundings. You see, Gwyneth, these daffodils would last much longer, if they were left to grow in the wild."

There was a long silence, then Gwyneth replied. "I believe what you say is right, Gareth! We ought to allow the flowers to grow in the woods. I always have an argument within myself. I want to pick wild Daffodils, Primroses, and Bluebells when I see them. Yet I know that after I pick them, they die so quickly, just as if they were unhappy at being taken out of the ground. Yes! I think that you are right! We ought to leave wild flowers just where they are.".

Gareth said, "My Dad once told me, that many years ago there was a countryman in the United States of America, known by the nick-name of "Johnny Apple-seed." He travelled about the country-side, planting apple-seeds. Everywhere the apple seeds grew up into apple trees. It would be a wonderful idea, if people, not only in Wales, but in England and Scotland planted trees, and flowers on St. David's day. Most of them would grow.

It would make Britain a beautiful place. It would be a good way to remember St. David of Wales."

Gwyneth went home from her visit to the hospital, feeling that she had learnt something on that St. David's day. Gareth was allowed home again from hospital, three weeks afterwards. There were still Daffodils growing in the mountain Glen.

Next time you climb a hill, and look down on the fields, towns and villages, just think that long ago, most of Britain was once covered by an enormous forest. Animals, large and small, lived among the trees. We have lost most of that forest, and most of the animals too. Few of the wild flowers remain. Let us take care of our rural environment.

Prayer:

Lord, we thank you for St. David of Wales.
We thank you for his faith and service,
to the Christian Church and people.
At this time of the year,
help us all to value our environment.
May we never harm the beauty of nature,
all around us.   Amen.

Hymn:

When your Father. (C&P.2. 73)

Teachers' Note: (1) We all inherit a precious religious history, handed down to us from people such as St. David. (2). We also inherit a natural environment from people of a past age. (3) We ought to value our religious and our natural surroundings.

(b) St. Patrick's Day   *Week 11   Three Saints Days*

St. Patrick is the Patron Saint of Ireland. In the church calender, March 17th. is kept as his special day. On that day, people wear the little green three leaf plant, called the "Shamrock." Again, it is difficult to say exactly where Patrick was born. We can be sure that it was somewhere on the West side of Britain, between Dumbarton on the river Clyde, and the Severn river, and South Wales. (The actual place name was known as Bannavem Taburniae). We know that Patrick's Grandfather was a Priest, and that his father was a Deacon in the Church. So the young Patrick was brought up as a Christian. Patrick was born about the year 390. A.D.

One dark night, Irish Pirates invaded from about one hundred ships. They landed on the shore, not far from Patrick's home. The Pirates killed many of the people, and stole everything they could steal. People put up a fight against the Pirates, but they were over-powered. The Pirates stole the cattle, and loaded them into their ships. They also captured many of the younger people, taking them back to Ireland as slaves. On that frightening night, Patrick as a young boy of 16 years of age, was carried off by sea to become a slave in Ireland.

He became a shepherd boy, on a hill, called "Slemish" in County Antrim. For six years he had to serve his Irish master. When Patrick was alone he used to pray to God. As he prayed, he came to realise that God had allowed him to be captured, because he had been chosen to become a missionary. The Irish people were pagan people, ruled by Druids. (Pagan Priests). The Irish people had not yet heard about the Church or Jesus Christ.

One night, in a dream, Patrick heard a voice, telling him to escape, because there was a ship waiting, and ready to take him across the sea. Patrick escaped, and travelled many days on foot along the sea coast. He found a ship which carried a cargo of Irish Wolf hounds. These dogs were to be sold in France. Patrick joined the crew, and worked his passage across in the ship. They finally landed in France.

Patrick was educated in Church matters in France, and later came back to England. He was sent to Ireland as a missionary. Patrick was a very successful missionary in Ireland. He raised up Christian churches and schools all over the country. On one occasion, he was trying to explain to the people about the Christian doctrine of the Trinity. (That God was one God in three persons. Father, Son ,and Holy spirit.) Patrick picked up a little green plant from the grass. It was one plant, but it had three leaves, very like a clover plant. He pointed out that God was one, yet three persons, just as one shamrock could have three leaves. Ever since, on the 17th. March, people wear the Shamrock. We must never forget that it was the Irish missionaries who brought the Church to Scotland and to the Northern parts of England.

Prayer:

> We thank you God for St. Patrick.
> We thank you for the meaning of the Shamrock.
> We thank you that St. Patrick,
> spread the good news about Jesus.
> Bring peace to the people of Ireland,
> and give us peace in our hearts.   Amen.

Hymn:

> The family of man. (C&P.l. 69)

Teachers' Note: (l) Patrick had a good religious up-bringing as a boy. (2). Patrick even when he was a slave and a shepherd knew how to pray to God. Young people may pray. (3) Patrick became a successful missionary teacher and scholar in the Irish (Gaelic) language. Probably, he used the six years when he was a slave to learn this language. God really was preparing Patrick to lead the Irish Church.

(c) St. Andrew

St. Andrew is the Patron Saint of Scotland. St. Andrew's day is held on 30th. November. His name in Greek means "a manly person". Andrew was a fisherman, working his boat from Capernaum, a town by the Sea of Galilee. He was the brother of Simon Peter, who also was a fisherman. One day Jesus said, "Follow me and I will make you fishers of men." Andrew obeyed the call of Jesus. (Andrew had been a disciple of John the Baptist.) It was Andrew who introduced Peter to Jesus. Both men became disciples of Jesus. Andrew possessed a special skill in bringing people together. Once when certain Greek people came inquiring about Jesus, it was Andrew who arranged their first meeting with him.

Andrew became famous because of the part he played in the feeding of the five thousand. The people had been following Jesus around the Lake shore. They sat down on the green grass. The large crowd became hungry. They were far away from the shops, from which they could buy food. Jesus told the people to sit down. There were about five thousand people. The disciples knew that the people were hungry. They told Jesus that they had not enough money anyway, to feed so many people.

Andrew saw a lad in the crowd, who had brought his lunch with him. He had five loaves, and two small fishes to eat that day. Probably, the lunch was prepared for him by his mother. It was Andrew who brought and introduced the lad to Jesus. The boy gave his lunch to Jesus, and Jesus prayed over it, and gave thanks. (In a similar way to how we say Grace before meals). After the prayer, Jesus performed a miracle, and there was enough food to feed all the people. The disciples distributed the loaves and fishes among the rows of sitting people. After the meal was over, the disciples gathered up twelve baskets of fragments lying about. Did you notice that it was Andrew who knew how to talk to the boy that day?

The four Gospels say more about Peter, James, and John, than they do about Andrew. He was the kind of person who could readily take the second place of importance. He did not easily become upset because he had been passed over. After Jesus died and went back to Heaven, Andrew became a preacher in Greece. Andrew was crucified because he was a Christian. However, his cross was shaped like an X. His arms and legs were tied to this saltire cross. (Saltire means shaped like a stile in a fence.) It is said, that he died after two days hanging on this cross.

Years afterward, a story arose, which told how St. Andrew's bones were carried to Scotland on a sailing ship, and buried at the town now called St. Andrews. When Scottish people became Christians, they adopted St. Andrew as their patron saint. The flag of Scotland is a white diagonal cross on a deep blue background. Next time you see a Union Jack flag, look at it closely. There are three crosses on it. The cross of St. George, the cross of St. Patrick, and the cross of St. Andrew.

St. Andrew's cross is like the sign we write for a kiss. There was once a little boy who went to a church in Scotland, which had a stained glass window depicting St. Andrew's Cross. The boy used to tell people that he went to the church with the kiss the window!

Prayer:

> Lord, we thank you for St. Andrew,
> and for his skill in bringing people together.
> May we also learn to introduce people as friends.
> We remember the lad who gave his lunch to Jesus.
> Make each of us aware that wc also,
> may become useful to others.
> Make us all brave and true like St. Andrew.   Amen.

Hymn:

> I will make you fishers of men. (JP. 123)

Teachers' Note: The story of the feeding of the five thousand is found in all four Gospels. (Matthew 9, Mark 6, Luke 9, and John 6). (1) Andrew was a very useful kind of "link-person" to have in a group. He must have had a pleasant personality. (2) Andrew had time to notice young people in the crowd. Young people would have trusted Andrew. (3) Maybe Andrew took literally the words of Jesus, "Follow me and I will make you fishers of men (people)". This was his gift.

(a) Palm Sunday

Week 12   Towards Easter

Long, long, before Jesus appeared in history, the Prophets of the Old Testament often acted-out parables to the people. This was probably because ordinary people in those days could not read or write. (Parables were stories with a meaning in them.) If they were acted-out, people could understand the meaning. Just as children sometimes act out a story at the school Worship Assembly.

The Sunday before Easter Sunday is called "Palm Sunday". On Palm Sunday, Jesus was really acting a parable before the people of the city of Jerusalem. They certainly understood what he meant by his actions.

First of all, Jesus sent two disciples to a house in another village, to bring back a donkey. When they reached the house, they found the donkey tethered to a post. Jesus had told the two disciples that if anyone asked them what they were doing, that they should answer that Jesus had need of the animal. This means that Jesus must have deliberately prepared beforehand for this special day.

When the disciples brought the donkey back to Jesus, some of the disciples put their coats across the donkey's back. Then Jesus mounted the donkey. This was a donkey that no-one had ever ridden before. When anyone rides a horse or a donkey for the first time, usually the animal is very nervous. It may jump about, and be very hard to control. On this occasion, the donkey remained very peaceful indeed. Jesus rode through the narrow streets of Jerusalem.

When the people saw Jesus they came out to welcome him. They shouted, "Hosanna! Blessed is he who comes in the name of the Lord. Hosanna in the highest." Many people broke off palm branches, and waved them as Jesus passed by. Jesus came riding on a donkey, because any King who came riding through his kingdom on a donkey, usually came in peace. If a King came to make war, then he would have come on a horse. Therefore, the people immediately understood the meaning of the acted parable. Jesus was coming to them as their King of peace!

Then Jesus went into the Temple. He saw many merchants and people there. Pigeons, and other animals for sacrifice, were being sold for the gain of the people who sold them. Money changers were doing a roaring trade, exchanging money for Temple coins to buy the pigeons. Again the merchants kept the profit for themselves. Jesus became very angry, because he knew that people were being cheated. He told the people, that the Scriptures had said, that his Father's house was to be a place of prayer, but they had made it to be a den of robbers.

Then he drove them all out of the Temple. He also drove the animals out, and over-turned the tables of the money changers. The Priests were very angry at Jesus, because he had stopped them gaining money for themselves in the Temple courtyard. They planned that they would kill Jesus when they had the next opportunity.

Often on Palm Sunday, at the morning Church service, the children walk in a procession around the church, carrying Palm leaves, to remind everyone of what happened when Jesus entered Jerusalem. Have you ever seen the cross on a donkey's back? Ask yourself whether it reminds you of anything?

Prayer:

> Father, God, we remember that our Lord Jesus,
> rode through the streets of Jerusalem,
> in a humble manner, seated on a donkey.
> We remember that the people welcomed him,

shouting "Hosanna" to the King of Peace.
Give us peace in our hearts and minds,
and may we be at peace with each other.   Amen.

Hymn:

Trotting, trotting. (C&P.2. 128)

Teachers' Note: "Hosanna" does not mean "Hurray." It means "Save us now."
(Sometimes we pray and we do not realise it.) The story is found in Matthew
Ch.21. Mark Ch.ll. Luke Ch.l9. and John Ch.12. (1) This is an acted parable.
There is scope here for mime and drama. Palm leaves may be made from paper,
or any long green leaves may be used. Jesus was enacting Zechariah 9;9. "Rejoice
greatly, daughter of Zion! Shout daughter of Jerusalem! Behold your king comes
riding upon an ass." (2) The important aspect is that Jesus comes in peace. (3)
The story of the cleansing of the Temple shows us that we may be angry when
wrong is being done deliberately to someone else.

(b) Good Friday   *Week 12   Towards Easter*

On the Thursday evening, Jesus and his disciples had shared a meal in the
upstairs room of the house belonging to a friend. At the meal Jesus had told the
disciples that one of them sitting at the table was a traitor, and that he would
would betray him. The disciples were shocked, and began to ask, who it was.
Jesus said, "It is he who has dipped his hand in the dish with me." Judas said,
"Lord is it I"? Jesus answered "Yes". Judas rose up from the table and went out
into the darkness of the night.

After the meal, Jesus tried to warn the disciples about what was going to
happen. He told them that they would become afraid, and leave him. Peter was
always the outspoken disciple. He boasted to Jesus that he would never leave
him. Jesus, told Peter, that he would deny him three times that night, before the
cock crowed.

They left the upper room, and went out into the night. Jesus took Peter, James,
and John, and went to the Garden of Gethsemane. This place was an Olive
orchard. Here, he asked the three disciples to watch and pray along with him. A
little way further into the garden, he knelt alone and prayed to God very intensely.

The three disciples had fallen asleep, when a crowd of soldiers and officials
arrived from the Chief Priests. They were carrying lights, swords, and clubs.
Judas was among them. He had agreed to lead them to Jesus for a reward of thirty
pieces of silver. Judas had given them a secret sign, saying, " Whoever I kiss on
the side of the cheek, he is the one to arrest." (This was how people greeted each

other in those days, instead of shaking hands). Judas drew near and greeted Jesus. The soldiers arrested Jesus and took him to the High Priest's house.

Peter had followed in the darkness, and entered the courtyard of the house. He stood beside the fire warming himself, with the servants. A girl servant asked him if he were not one of the followers of Jesus the Nazarene. Peter denied it. Later, someone else asked him the same question. Again Peter denied that he had anything to do with Jesus. A third time, another servant said, "Surely, you are one of his followers. Did I not see you in the garden?" Peter was afraid, and denied that he had been with Jesus. Just at that moment, the cock began to crow! Peter remembered what Jesus had said. "Before the cock crows once, you will deny me three times." He left the courtyard in tears.

Jesus was tried in a court, first before Pilate the Governor. Then Pilate sent Jesus to King Herod. The soldiers put a crown of thorns on Jesus' head, and a purple robe on him. They knelt down and mocked Jesus, pretending that he was a king. Herod sent Jesus back to Pilate, who could not find any crime that Jesus had committed. He took a basin of water, and washed his hands before the people. (Meaning that he was washing his hands of the case.)

Pilate had another prisoner who was a robber and a murderer, called "Barabbas". Pilate brought Barrabas out of prison, and asked the crowd outside, "Whom will I set free? Barabbas or Jesus?" The crowd shouted that he should set Barabbas free, and crucify Jesus. Pilate gave Jesus to the soldiers to be whipped. Then the soldiers led Jesus along with two other robbers through the streets of Jerusalem, and outside the city gates, to a hill called Calvary. Jesus was so weak that when he was carrying his cross he fell down. The soldiers compelled a man in the crowd, named Simon of Cyrene to carry the cross for Jesus.

The soldiers nailed Jesus on a cross, between the crosses of the other two robbers. One of the robbers insulted Jesus. The other dying robber said, "Lord remember me when you come into your kingdom." Jesus answered him, "Today, you will be with me in Paradise". The crowd around the cross mocked Jesus, saying, "If you are the Christ, come down from the cross, and we will believe you." Jesus prayed that God would forgive them for their cruelty.

Jesus became very thirsty. A soldier soaked a sponge in sour wine, and held it up on a stick to the mouth of Jesus. Jesus refused the wine. He had been hanging on the cross from about nine o'clock in the morning, until about three o'clock in the afternoon. Mary the mother of Jesus, and John the apostle were standing near the cross, watching sadly. Jesus prayed, "Father, into your hands I commit my spirit." He then closed his eyes and died.

Prayer:

> Father, God, we feel very sad,
> about the cruel cross.
> We do not understand why people
> should have rejected the Lord Jesus,
> and sent him to his death.
> Yet, we thank you for the cross,
> because in the death of Jesus,
> we see the love of God for each of us.   Amen.

Hymn:

> Lord of the dance. (C&P.l. 22)

Teachers' Note: (1) There is no orthodox doctrine of the crucifixion. It may be explained in many ways. Jesus in his life reveals God's love for people. Jesus in his death also loved people. Children can understand love. (2) It is sad that the friends of Jesus were so weak and afraid. Later, when they understood, they became strong in faith. (3) The cross teaches us to forgive people when they treat us wrongly.

(c) Easter Morning   *Week 12   Towards Easter*

After Jesus died, he was buried not in a grave in the ground, but in a tomb cut out of the rock. A great stone was placed at the door of the tomb. Joseph of Arimathea was a secret disciple of Jesus. He went to Pilate, the governor and asked that the body of Jesus should be placed in his garden tomb. The result was that Jesus, who was a poor man, was buried in a rich man's tomb.

Very early on Sunday morning, the women came bringing spices to put in the tomb. They found that the stone had been rolled away from the entrance, and that the body was gone. An angel had already rolled the stone away. The women were very frightened. The angel spoke to them. "You are looking for Jesus. He is not here. He has risen from the dead. See here is where his body was lying. Go now and tell his friends the news."

When the women went back and told the disciples what had happened, the men did not believe them. They thought that the women had imagined everything. Peter and John ran to the tomb to see for themselves what had happened. John was a faster runner than Peter, and he reached the garden tomb first. He looked in, but John did not dare to go in himself. When Peter arrived, out of breath, both the men went in to the tomb. They looked at the cloths on the ground which had been around the body. They saw that the cloth which had been around the head of

Jesus, was neatly folded, and set apart. They realised that the women were telling the truth. Jesus had arisen from the dead.

John and Peter went back to their homes. Mary Magdalene had followed the men to the tomb, but she did not go home. Instead, she remained outside the tomb quietly crying. She looked inside the tomb, and she saw two angels dressed in white, standing inside at the two opposite ends of the grave. The angels asked her, "Woman, why are you crying?" Mary said, "They have taken my Lord away, and I do not know where they have taken him".

Mary turned round and she saw a man standing. She thought it was the gardener. (The stranger really was Jesus.) He asked her the same question. "Woman why are you crying? " Mary answered, "Sir, if you have taken him away, tell me where you have put him." Jesus said to her one word only. "Mary," he whispered. Mary Magdalene immediately recognised the voice of Jesus. She called out joyfully, "Teacher"! She clung to Jesus. Jesus told Mary to go back and tell all his friends, that he had risen from the dead. Mary went back to the disciples with the happy news. "I have seen the Lord!" She told them everything that had happened to her.

Later that very day, another two men were walking to the village of Emmaus, which was about seven miles outside Jerusalem. They too had been disciples of Jesus. They were feeling very sad about the death of their Teacher. A stranger came alongside them, as they walked. He asked them why they were so sad. They told the stranger how Jesus had been crucified on the Friday. The stranger explained to them that the Prophets wrote in the scriptures that all this would happen.

The two men invited the stranger into their house for a meal. It was evening, and becoming dark. When the stranger held the bread in his hands, and gave a prayer of thanks for it, they realised that the stranger was Jesus. Then he disappeared out of the room. The two men walked the seven miles back to Jerusalem that evening, to bring the happy news that they had seen Jesus.

Often at Easter time, children eat chocolate Easter eggs. Years ago poorer children received a real hard boiled egg on Easter Sunday. Many people collected the yellow flower from the Broom or Gorse bushes which grow wild in Britain. They boiled the flower leaves along with the egg, to make a harmless dye. When they took the egg out of the pot, they had a yellow hard-boiled egg. An old custom was to roll your egg down a hill to celebrate Easter.

The meaning of the old custom was to remind themselves, that just as a chicken comes out of the egg alive, so Jesus came out of the tomb alive. Just as the stone was rolled away. So we roll the egg down the hill to remember Easter time. Did you know that the Jewish religion kept the seventh day, (Saturday) as their holy day, which they called the "Sabbath". Christians keep the first day of the week (Sunday) as the Christian Sabbath, because Jesus arose from the dead on the first day of the week. The first disciples called Sunday the "Lord's Day".

Prayer:

> Lord God, our Father in Heaven,
> we thank you for the first Easter morning,
> when Jesus arose from the dead.
> We thank you for the Christian Sabbath.
> Help us to use Sunday as a happy day,
> for rest and recreation.   Amen.

Hymn:

> Now the green blade rises. (C&P.2. 131)

Teachers' Note: What happened on the first Easter Day has several differing accounts in the four Gospels. (1) Easter teaches a mystery, that God is stronger than evil or even death. (2) Easter gives everyone new hope. (3) Easter for Christians is the most important time of the year, because if there had not been a Resurrection, there would have been no Christian religion. (Christianity does not depend on the cross, but on the message of Easter.)

Summer Term

(a) The Wild-Life Pond

Stewart and Fiona were brother and sister. Stewart was about eleven years of age, and Fiona was eight years of age. The garden behind their house was a large one. It had high trees growing at one end. Bushes and flowers grew all around it. Their Dad and Mum decided to made a wild-life pond at the bottom of the garden for them.

First, they dug a large hole at the bottom of the garden. They found this to be very hard work. Everyone helped with the digging. They made the pond water-tight, by using a large plastic sheet, to line the inside of the hole. Then, they had to carry in buckets some rather smelly, older, water from the canal to mix with the tap water in the pond. When they had mixed the two kinds of water, the bacteria in the mixed water began slowly to increase. After a few weeks, little creatures began to appear in the pond. Water weeds began to grow.

Stewart and Fiona went with their Parents to the Lake District. They found a muddy marsh with a very slow-flowing stream in it. Floating on top of the water they discovered Frog-spawn. The Frog-spawn was composed of a mass of jelly-like eggs all joined together. Each egg had a tiny black dot in the middle of the jelly-like eggs. These black dots were the baby frogs, which would grow later when the weather became warmer.

Stewart and Fiona put a small quantity of the Frog-spawn into their bucket, being careful to leave plenty in the wild! They brought it back in the car. They put the Frog-spawn into their garden pond. After a month had passed, they noticed that the eggs were turning into Tadpoles. The Tadpoles were swimming about the pond like tiny fish. A few more weeks passed by, and the Tadpoles had turned into tiny Frogs. These Frogs grew bigger every week. Many other insects were now growing in the wild-life pond. The Frogs were very happy in their new home. The more the Frogs ate the other little insects, the more insects seemed to multiply in the pond.

During the hot Summer, a Grey Heron happened to see a large Frog moving on a rock at the side of the pond. The Grey Heron being hungry, flew down and gobbled up the Frog. All the other Frogs were wise enough to hide under the leafy bushes and long grass around the pond. Stewart and Fiona were upset because the Grey Heron had eaten one of the Frogs. They chased it away.

Their Father explained that this was how the food-chain worked in Nature. Bacteria devoured each other. The insects ate the bacteria, which was often so small that it could not be seen with the human eye. Then the Frogs ate the insects. The Grey Heron was hungry, so it ate up the Frog. Stewart and Fiona began to understand that everything in the environment is a part of something else in the environment. (Food chain). So they never put Henry, their pet Gold-fish in the pond, because if the Grey Heron did not eat him, the cat next door might eat him instead!

When Parents and their children make a wild-life pond, they are making a suitable environment for wild life. Can you make a list of the things which make up your environment?

First, everyone needs fresh air to breathe. We need somewhere to live; a house, or a caravan, or a tent, or a cave, to keep out the weather. We need to be kept warm. In our houses some means of heating (gas or electric) are used to keep us warm.

We would die of thirst if we had no water supply. We need rest, since every bird and animal goes to sleep. We all need a warm bed. We need water to keep us clean and healthy.

Goldfish in our homes need food. It is usually supplied by the owner of the Goldfish. Birds need food. They bring worms and insects to their young fledglings. Someone in our environment has to go to the grocers, butchers, bakers, and fish shops to buy food to eat. Sometimes, it is Mum, sometimes it is Dad, who brings the food home for the family. (Children can help to do this!)

Birds teach their little ones to fly from the nest. Ducks teach a brood of little ducklings how to swim in the river or canal. Parents teach little children how to walk, or to use a spoon, or to button their coats. Children also need a learning environment. This is the reason why we attend school.

A good environment is very important for all of us. We ought to be thankful, that we live in a beautiful country. We have clean water, food, clothing, houses, and schools. Let us all protect our environment by not spoiling any part of it, because the environment is our home, and the home of children in the future too.

Prayer:

> Lord, we thank you, for the lovely environment of nature.
> We thank you, lakes, rivers, canals, and wild life ponds;
> for green fields, and blue skies;
> for the clean sea, and the golden sand.
> We thank you, for Parents, and a good caring school.
> We pray for children who live
> in a poorer environment than ourselves.   Amen.

Hymn:

> God in his love. (C&P.2. 76)

Teachers' Note: (1) Making a wild life pond needs adult advice and help. (Children should not attempt taking water from canals.) (2) Every creature in Nature has its own food chain as a part of its own environment. (3) Children also have a physical and a cultural environment. There is a difference between what we want and what we need!

(b) Coming Home Again

Did you know that both your feet are not exactly the same size? Have you ever looked at people when they are walking? People walk in different ways. If we walk across a field with our eyes shut, we would soon learn that we do not walk in straight lines. In Canada there are vast areas of very flat countryside called "Prairies." Wheat is grown on them in Summer. Sometimes there are no trees growing on the horizon whatsoever. In the Winter time the snow falls very heavily, and it lies on the ground for a long time. So if you go for a walk in the snow, there are no land marks to follow.

Here is a story about two Farmers who lived in a Log Cabin on the edge of the Prairie land. It had been snowing heavily, and then it had stopped. The two men went for a walk, but the snow came on again, thick and fast, falling from the sky like Goose feathers. They could not see any landmark. There were no trees, bushes, or houses, or telegraph poles. They were lost on the snowy Prairie. They were afraid to stop walking, in case they died with the cold. Instead they decided that they would walk, and continue to walk in a straight line, until they reached another farm ahead of them somewhere.

The two Farmers walked all day, and they saw nothing but snow. Not even a Wolf was about. They walked all day, and all night long, trying to keep in a straight line, until in the morning, they came to a farm house. When they reached the front door, they knocked the front door very loudly. No-one answered the door. Then they turned the door handle, and walked in to the farm house.

They discovered that they were in their own house again. Instead of walking in a straight line, as they had thought, they had really walked in a circle, without knowing it. They were very relieved that they were so fortunate, and that they were safe home again. Looking up at the picture hanging over the fireplace, they reads the words. "East or West, Home is best!"

Children walk in a kind of a circle, when in the morning they go to school, and when they arrive back home again in the afternoon. We ought to be thankful for our homes. John Howard Payne wrote the words, "Be it ever so humble, there is no place like home".

There is a story told about a lady who was very discontented. She lived by the sea-side, in a little sandy bay, which curved like a half-moon. She used to look across the sea to the other side of the bay. She could see a lovely little cottage, with golden windows. The sun shone on the cottage, and made a reflection (like a mirror) that could be seen miles away.

The discontented lady used to say to herself. "I wish I lived in that lovely cottage with the golden windows across the bay. I think I would be the happiest person in all the world". One day she decided to take a walk round the bay to have a closer look at the cottage with the golden windows. She planned to walk one way out, and to return by home by bus in the evening.

The discontented lady had a beautiful walk, around the sandy bay, and finally, she reached the cottage. It was early evening. She was very disappointed to find that the cottage, which she so admired, had no golden windows after all. They were just ordinary glass! As she stood, she happened to look back across the sandy bay, to her own cottage. To her surprise, the sun was shining on it, and her cottage had beautiful golden windows. She realised that the sun had shone on her own cottage every day of her life, and she had never noticed it before. The discontented lady went home in the bus that evening, and she was never discontented again.

Prayer:

> Father God, we thank you for our homes.
> We thank you for warmth, and our food;
> for friends and loved ones.
> We pray for any people who have no homes,
> or who live in poverty.
> Make us more contented, and grateful.   Amen.

Hymn:

> Sad, puzzled eyes. (C&P.2. 74)

Teachers' Notes: (1). Childrens' homes may vary in many ways, depending on economics and culture. To the child it ought to be home sweet home. (A place to return to for love and security.) (2) Contentment at home is more valuable than, "Trying to keep up with the Jones". (3) We should never forget the plight of people who are homeless.

(c) The Boy Who Ran Away From Home   *Week 1   Our Homes*

Jesus told a story about a farmer who lived on his farm with his two sons. The younger son did not like the farm. He became discontented. He had heard tales about how good life was in the far country. One day he said to his Father, "Father, give me my share of the farm estate?" The father divided his property between the two sons. The younger son took his share, and turned it into money.

He was now very wealthy. He left his Father and elder brother on the farm, while he travelled to the far country.

Because he had plenty of money, he had many companions. He went on a spending spree, and squandered all his money on foolish pleasures. When his money was all spent, his companions left him. They were no longer interested in him, since his money was finished. A famine spread all over the country. There was a shortage of food, and people everywhere were starving. The younger son took the only job he could find, looking after pigs. Often he was so hungry, that he could have eaten food which the pigs were eating.

He became home-sick. Then he came to his senses. He thought to himself, "this is indeed a foolish situation. My Father's servants have more than enough to eat, and here I am, starving. I will go back home. I will say to my Father, that I have sinned, and that I am not worthy to be his son. Perhaps, he will give me a job."

Unknown to the younger son, his Father had often looked down that road, hoping his son might return. When he was a long way off the Farm, his father saw him wearily walking home. His Father ran to meet him. Throwing his arms around his son, he hugged and kissed him, and made him welcome. The son felt ashamed, and said, "Father I have sinned against Heaven and against you. I am not fit to be called your son." The Father called out to his servants, "Bring new clothes, put a ring on his finger, and shoes on his feet. Bring the fattened calf, and kill it. We must have a great feast to celebrate. I thought that my son here, was dead. Now he is alive again. He was lost. Now he has been found!"

The elder brother was in the field. He heard the music and the dancing in the house. He asked one of the servants what was happening. The servant answered, "Your brother has come home. Your Father has killed the fatted calf for the meal. Everyone is happy." The elder brother became very angry, and he would not go in to the celebrations. "He said to his Father, "All these years I have worked for you. I have always obeyed you. You did not even give me a young goat, so that I could celebrate with my friends. Now that this no-good son has returned, after squandering all his money, you have made a feast for him."

The Father answered the elder son, "Son all that I have is yours. We had to have a celebration, because this is your brother, who has returned. Your brother was dead, and is alive again. He was lost, and has been found."

Prayer:

> Lord, we thank you for the story of the Prodigal Son.
> It reminds us that God is our Father,
> and that God loves each one of his family.
> Teach us not to waste our gifts and talents.

If we make mistakes in life,
show us that God is ready to forgive us.   Amen.

Hymn:

When Jesus walked in Galilee. (C&P.l. 25)

Teachers' Note: The story is found in St. Luke, Gospel, Chapter 15, and naturally divides into three parts. (Sick of home.) (Home-sick). (Home again). (1) The younger son is unhappy at home. Consider possible reasons for this unhappiness. (2) The younger son reaches the land of his dreams. He wastes his wealth and ends up eating pig food. He thinks of home. (3) The younger son returns home to his forgiving Father, and his unforgiving brother.

(a) Walking on Wheels   *Week 2   Learning*

Mandy was six years old, when her Parents bought her a new yellow mountain bike as a Christmas present. The weather was so wet and stormy during the months of January and February, that she never had an opportunity to learn to ride it. Mandy had dreams about her mountain bike, and in her dreams, she dreamt that her legs were moving the pedals but the bike remained still. She just could not get the wheels to turn round. She would wake out of her dream, crying in her sleep.

When the month of March came round, the weather became dry, and a little windy. Mandy asked her elder brother, Wayne, to teach her to ride the bike on the following Saturday morning. She knew that she would not be at school on a Saturday. Her Dad would be at his work in town. Mandy was very nervous about the thought of learning to ride. She worried whether she might fall off the bike.

When Saturday morning arrived, Wayne got up early, and wakened Mandy. "Wakey, wakey, Mandy!" he said. "This is the day, when you are going to learn to ride your new mountain bike." Mandy jumped out of bed, washed and dressed herself very quickly. She finished her breakfast. Then she felt nervous again. She had a funny feeling in her tummy. She told her brother, Wayne, how she felt. Wayne smiled at Mandy, and he said, "Mandy, if you are going to ride a bike, then you will have to do it yourself." That made Mandy feel even more nervous.

Mandy knew her highway code. She had a good memory for books. Wayne had asked her about road signs, and about white lines painted on the road. Mandy knew all the answers. She knew how to put her hand out to signal going to the right, or to the left. She could pump up a tyre. She knew how to ring the bell. Yet she had never been on a bike before.

Wayne took the Bike out of the garage, and he adjusted the seat to the proper height. Then Mandy sat on the Bike, and Wayne held his hand behind the seat, to steady her so that she would not fall over. Wayne gave her the advice, "When you are on a bike, you do not look at the front wheel, but at the road or path ahead of you." Off they went down the level foot path. Mandy was pedalling, and at the same time trying to keep her balance. She was terrified. Wayne walked at a quick pace, holding on to the bike as Mandy moved her legs.

Six times they went up and down the long foot-path. Mandy wobbled at first, but soon she learned not to look at her front wheel. She began to take care as she went around the corner and back again. Pedalling up the street for the seventh time, she asked Wayne whether she was doing well. No answer came! Mandy looked back quickly, to discover that Wayne was not behind her holding the seat. She realised that she was pedalling alone. She could hear Wayne shouting, "Keep your legs moving. Don't stop, Mandy!" She saw another big boy come towards her on his bike, so she gently pulled on her brakes a little, and carried on.

A great sense of joy and happiness came over her. Her nervous feeling had gone. "I can ride a mountain bike, hip, hip, hurray, she shouted, as she waved one hand in the air. Mandy had forgotten to keep her balance, and she looked down at her front wheel. It wobbled, and Mandy fell off with a bump. Her knees were scraped a little on the rough gravel. Mandy was excited, forgetting about her sore knees, she turned the bike around. She sat on the seat again, and pedalled back down the street to Wayne. He gave her an encouraging smile.

Wayne said, "Well done Mandy! Some things you have to learn by yourself. Now you can ride a bike!" Mandy knew at last that she could ride her beautiful yellow mountain bike! The last lesson Wayne gave her, was to show her how to lock up her bike with a padlock and chain.

The bad dream never came back to Mandy. Instead, she had many other dreams. They were happy dreams. Mandy woke up in the mornings with the feeling that she was the happiest girl in the world.

Children learn many things with the help of other children. On other occasions children need a grown-up person, such as a Parent or Teacher to teach them. Sometimes a clever way for children to learn good things, is to watch a good person whom they admire. We have to be careful not to imitate the bad habits of people. Sometimes we need a pattern to imitate. When Jesus was alive, the people who followed him were called "disciples." This word "disciple" means "learner". Often, the disciples called Jesus "Teacher." On one occasion in the Gospels he said, "Learn of me!" The point about learning anything is that you must put part of yourself into what you want to learn.

Prayer:

> Lord, we thank you for the ability to learn.
> Help us to be respectful to our Parents.
> May we learn from our Teachers at school.
> May we learn good habits from our friends.
> May we learn from the Bible.
> Open our eyes to learn from Nature.   Amen.

Hymn:

> Black and white. (C&P.l. 67)

Teachers' Note: (1) Children naturally want to learn. A good way to learn is to ask questions. (2) Children may learn from other children, especially older members of the family. (3) Children may learn many things for themselves. (such as riding a bike, reading a book, personal faith, and personal praying).

(b) Learning to Forgive
Week 2   Learning

The Village Parish Council decided to hold a Gardening competition with two prizes. One prize was for the best kept adult's garden. The other prize was a Childrens' Prize for the best children's garden. Lucy and Peter decided to enter the competition. They had a small garden at the rear of their house. They dug over the ground very carefully. They planted various kinds of flowers. There was a wall behind their garden, where they planted Sweet Pea seeds. In the Spring time, the flowers grew up very quickly. Best of all, their Sweet Pea plants grew high, climbing up the wall. They grew higher than Lucy and Peter. On one bright sunny day, the Sweet Pea plants began to produce flowers, on almost every stem. They looked beautiful. Red, purple, yellow, blue, white, and pink flowers were growing high against the wall. Marjorie and Peter were very proud of their garden.

Tim lived in the next house. He was not interested in gardening. Instead, he kept rabbits in hutches. Tim loved his rabbits, and he fed them every day before he went to school. He was a good boy, and very friendly with Lucy and Peter. Then an unfortunate accident happened! One day when the children were at school, one of Tim's rabbits escaped out of its hutch. The rabbit crawled through the hedge, and went into Lucy and Peter's garden. The rabbit was hungry, and it began to nibble at the bottom of the row of Sweet Pea plants. The rabbit ate its way along the row. When the two children came back from school, they saw that all the Sweet Pea plants had been eaten away at the bottom. The tall stems were now falling down. The beautiful flowers were dying.

Lucy and Peter were very angry, because they knew that they had lost any hope of winning the Garden Competition. When Tim returned home from school, he noticed that his hutch door was open. His rabbit was gone. The three children met in Lucy and Peter's garden. Tim was blamed for not keeping the hutch door securely locked. Angry words were said. "Lucy scolded Tim, saying "I will never forgive you, because you have spoiled our Prize garden." Tom found his rabbit, and climbed back over the wall into his own garden. The Children never spoke to each other for many weeks.

Lucy and Peter kept a beautiful blue and green budgie in a cage. It could talk, and it could say, "Billy is a pretty boy." They often opened the door of the cage, and allowed the budgie to fly around the room. It always went back into its cage. One day Peter opened the cage door, and the Budgie flew round the room. Lucy did not know the budgie was out of its cage, as she came in from the garden. When she opened the back door, the budgie flew outside, and flew away. Both Lucy and Peter ran outside, but the bird was gone. They were very upset, because they loved their budgie.

Tim happened to come into his garden to clean out his rabbit hutches. He saw the two children crying in the garden. Tim climbed over the wall, and asked what had happened. The two children told him. Tim said, "Let us watch the other birds." The sparrows were making a fuss in the bushes and they were attacking the budgie. Tim called out to Lucy and Peter to bring the cage from their house. Tim took a long pole. He tied the cage on to the end of the pole.

When the sparrows attacked the budgie again, he very slowly held up the long pole with the cage tied to the end of it. He told Lucy and Peter to keep very still. The Budgie was terrified by the sparrows, so it flew up to its cage, and went inside. Tim slowly lowered the cage, and quickly closed the cage door. Lucy and Peter smiled and thanked Tim. "We would not have known what to do," Lucy said. Then she remembered that she was not supposed to be talking to Tim. She felt ashamed of herself. " She said, "Tim, we both forgive you! It was all an accident. Your rabbit escaped, just like our pet budgie. Yes, we forgive you! Thank you for helping us, even though maybe we did not deserve it".

Now it was Tim's turn to smile. He said, "I worried a lot, when you said that you would never forgive me. I thought that I had lost my two friends for ever. I am pleased now that we are friends again! 'Forgive' is a lovely word, isn't it!" The children smiled, and they never argued with each other again.

A disciple once asked Jesus, whether it was good to forgive seven times. Jesus said that we are to forgive, seventy times seven.

Prayer:

> Father God, may we all learn
> how to forgive other children,
> whom we think may have harmed, or hurt us.
> Lord, it is difficult to learn to forgive.
> Make us kind-hearted.
> Forgive us for our own mistakes.   Amen.

Hymn:

> Make me a channel of your peace. The prayer of St. Francis. (C&P.2. 147)

Teachers Notes: (1) To forgive is always very difficult, especially if we have been inwardly hurt. (2). We forget that we ourselves can do wrong actions, and also need God's forgiveness. (3) In the Lord's prayer, there is a sentence which says, "Forgive us our trespasses, as we forgive others their tresspasses."

(c) Learning in the Temple
Week 2   Learning

Joseph and Mary went up to the city of Jerusalem, because it was the Passover Festival. The Passover meal celebrated the time long ago when God rescued his people from Egypt.

The first Passover meal had been held in Egypt. The Hebrews had been slaves to the Egyptians, but they escaped during the night. The Egyptian army pursued them. The Hebrews found themselves with an Egyptian army behind them, and blocked by the Red sea stretched out before them. It looked as if every Hebrew slave would be killed by the pursuing Egyptian army. When the Hebrews reached the shore of the Red sea, God caused an East wind to blow, and it blew the sea back. The Hebrew people people crossed the sea on dry land. ("Hebrew people", is another name for the "Jewish people"). Since then, every year in the Spring time, Jewish people have killed a lamb, and eaten a special meal, to remind them of the first Passover.

This was the reason why Joseph and Mary made the journey to Jerusalem with their family. They wanted to spend the Festival in the holy city. Jesus at this time was twelve years of age. They spent a very happy time at Jerusalem. They met many old friends, and they made new ones. Then they set off on their journey homewards to the village of Nazareth. There was quite a number of other people returning with their families, and the crowd straggled along the narrow road. The boys were talking to each other as usual, as they walked in the crowd. Joseph and Mary did not notice that their son, Jesus, was not in the crowd, until that evening. They both were very worried, wondering what had happened to him.

Early next morning Joseph and Mary went back to Jerusalem, looking for their lost son. They did not find Jesus the first day. They spent a second day looking for their son. Now they became very anxious. On the third day they found Jesus in the Temple. (The Temple was the most important religious building in Jerusalem.) Jesus, although only a boy, was sitting listening to the learned men, who were Teachers of the Jewish scriptures. He was asking them questions. Everyone who heard the boy, Jesus, were amazed at his understanding, and the answers which he gave.

His Parents were astonished to find their son in the Temple. Mary, the mother of Jesus, said to her son, "Why have you treated us like this? Your father and I have been most anxious, searching for you all over the place". Jesus replied, "Why were you searching for me. Did you not know that I had to be in my Father's house?. Mary and Joseph were puzzled by the answers given by Jesus. There was always something deep and thoughtful about their boy. Jesus quite naturally spoke of God as his "Father".

The family returned to their home in Nazareth. Jesus was always obedient to his parents. He grew taller, and became wiser every day. Mary knew that her son was not just an ordinary boy. She listened to his sayings, and kept them like treasure in her heart.

Prayer:

Father God, teach us to learn about the our faith.

Teach us to respect the Church,

or Synagogue, or Mosque, or Temple,

or other holy building,

associated with our faith.

Help us to read God's Holy Book.   Amen.

Hymn:

Give us hope, Lord. (C&P.2. 87)

Teachers' Note: This story is found in St. Luke Chapter 2. verses 41-52. (1). Young people can cause their Parents much worry by not returning home when they are expected. Mary and Joseph's anxious search shows that that they dearly loved their son. (2) Christians believe that Jesus was just like other boys. Yet in a deeper way, as he grew up into manhood, Jesus was full of the goodness of God. (3) This story shows that young people too may develop an awareness of the presence of God.

(a) The "Thank You" Clock

Bill had been an engine driver on the Railways for forty years. When he reached the age to retire from work, he was very sorry, because he had loved driving the engines all over England. He had begun work on the railways as a boy. He became a Porter, and then a Guard, riding on the last coach of the train. He transferred from his job to become a fire-man on the old steam trains. His task was to shovel the coal into the engine furnace. The furnace boiled the water to make steam to drive the engine's pistons. Then at last, Bill was promoted to become an engine driver. Later he learnt to drive the newer diesel engines. He loved his job, even though he went to work very early in the morning, at six o'clock.

When Bill retired, the Manager made a little speech, and thanked him for his splendid record of good time-keeping, and good work, for the Railway Company. The Manager presented him with a beautiful chiming clock. Bill was very proud of the Clock, because it was the Railway Company's way of saying "Thank You". He kept the clock on his fire-place for everyone to see. There was a little brass plate on the front of the clock, with Bill's name written on it, and the length of service, "Forty years."

Bill's grandson was named Alex. He was eleven years of age. He loved his Grandad to tell him stories about the old steam engines which ran from London to Edinburgh. He knew all about the "Flying Scotsman," and its speed record. Alex came running home from school one day. "Grandad, I've good news for you. The Railway Company are allowing the Flying Scotsman to make a special run to Edinburgh on a Sunday, on the East Coast line. Will you allow me to take you? The school is putting on a special coach, and we are allowed to bring one adult. I'd really like you to come!"

Bill's eyes lit up. He had never expected to see the Flying Scotsman again. He said, "Do you know, that steam engine was built in 1923? It could scoop up water from underneath it, when it was moving. It had a little corridor into the Cab, from the back, so that another driver and fireman could take over, when the first two operators were tired. Alex, I'd love to see that engine just once more", "Right", said Alex, "I'll tell our Headteacher. You can sit next to me on the coach, Grandad."

At last the Sunday arrived, and the coach of children and adults set off on the journey for Darlington Railway Station, in County Durham. They arrived early, and had a good meal. There were thousands of people standing back from the railway track, waiting to see the famous steam engine pulling her carriages, and rushing through the station. The party of children and adults to which Alex and his Grandad belonged had reserved seats near the Darlington Station platform.

Everyone was excited. Alex felt butterflies in his tummy. People were waving flags. The Station-master and his Porters all were wearing their best uniforms. They were watching the signals, and waiting to hear the bell which would ring, to indicate that the Flying Scotsman was two miles up the line.

Then the signals changed to green. Everyone began to cheer, and a low thundering roar was heard along the lines. The huge engine came into view, belching a trailing cloud of steam, and blowing her whistle, as she came rushing through the station. The passengers were waving their hands. With a mighty roar, onwards the Flying Scotsman travelled to Edinburgh. What a wonderful sight it was! The cheering of the people who were watching was deafening. Alex looked up at Grandad's face. Grandad was crying tears of joy and happiness. Alex held his Grandad's hand very tightly.

On the way home in the school bus, the children and adults were smiling, but rather quiet. They felt it was a privilege, and good fortune, that they had been able to see for themselves, the famous railway steam engine from the past. Soon everyone was home again.

Next day, after school, Alex, went to visit his Grandad. They talked about the excitement of the previous Sunday at Darlington Station. Grandad, stood up, and gently lifted the presentation chiming clock in his hands. "Here", Alex, he said, "this is a "Thank You" clock. I am going to give you a "Thank You" present. I want you to have my clock. You can keep it safe at home in your own room. I am an old man now. I do not need it any more. I want to show you how thankful I am, for the happiest day I have spent in many years."

Alex carried the clock home very carefully. He was glad that his Grandad had appreciated seeing the Flying Scotsman again. He thought to himself, "I cannot take this Thank You clock for myself. I will keep it for a little while, and then I'll bring it back to Grandad's house. It was his special present from the railway."

Hymn:

Thank you, Lord. (C&P.l. 32)

Prayer:

Help us Lord, to make other people happy.
Let us never be selfish or unkind.
Teach us to have thankful hearts.
Give us a respect for older people,
who have served us well,
and have given us a good example.   Amen.

Teachers' Note: (1) Everyone who works for others is worthy of our respect, if they do their job well. (2) Young people can give pleasure to older people by being helpful in some kind way. (3) We may show our thankfulness by giving a present.

(b) Rewards   *Week 3   Being Thankful*

Mrs. Holroyd was the village Librarian. She was a widow. Her husband had died some years before she had taken on the job at the Library. She lived in a cottage beside the Library. She loved books, and encouraged the children to join the Library. She would advise anyone about good books to read. She loved the children to come to the Library, although she was very strict about borrowers not talking loudly. When people forgot, and spoke loudly, she would point to a large sign which read, "SILENCE PLEASE!" Most people thought that she was a splendid Librarian.

Wendy and Richard were twins. They had joined the Library, and often borrowed books. One day, they heard Mrs. Holroyd say to one of assistants. "A terrible thing has happened to me today. I have lost my wedding ring. I took it off yesterday, and I know that I put it on my finger at breakfast time. Somehow, it must have fallen off my finger. I was peeling potatoes early today, and maybe it has been thrown out with the potato skins. I have searched everywhere for it. I just cannot find it." Mrs. Holroyd was very disturbed about the loss of her ring.

Wendy and Richard, asked whether they could help to find the ring. Mrs. Holroyd was pleased, at their offer, and said, . "Yes, come round to the cottage this afternoon, and have a good look down the garden for me." Wendy and Richard rushed home from school, and searched the front and back gardens. Wendy said to Richard, "Maybe someone has stolen the ring." Richard laughed at Wendy, and said, "Do not be so silly. Burglars would have taken more than just one ring." His eye caught sight of Blackie the cat, chasing a Jackdaw out of the garden. "I hate cats, when they hunt the birds" he remarked. Wendy answered, "They cannot help it, it is just part of the cat's nature to hunt birds. I am sure that birds must have bad habits too."

They could not find the ring. Wendy and Richard told Mrs. Holroyd that they had searched everywhere for the ring, with no success. Mrs. Holroyd was very upset by this time. The twins went home, and later that evening they went to bed, just as usual. "Let us be real detectives, and try to solve this mystery," Wendy said. "There must be a clue somewhere."

Next morning Richard woke first. He had been thinking about the lost ring late into the night, before he went to sleep. When Wendy awoke, and came into his bedroom, he said to her, "Wendy I have had a terrible night last night, trying to sleep. I cannot get that ring out of my mind. Do you remember what you said about birds?" You said, that Birds have bad habits too! Richard asked, "What bad habits would a Jackdaw have?" Wendy smiled, and said, "That's the clue, we have missed! Jackdaws steal bright shiny things, and put them in their nest. Maybe the Jackdaw is the thief!

After school that day, they hurried back to Mrs. Holroyd's back garden. There was the Jackdaw, flying into a high bush. The twins found a ladder, and set it against the wall. They began to search for the Jackdaw's nest. They found it fairly high up in a bush near the wall. Wendy held the ladder, and Richard climbed up and looked into the Jackdaw's nest. He became very excited. There are safety pins in here, and a piece of old broken mirror, and a gold ring in bottom of the nest. Carefully, he took the ring out of the nest, and down to Wendy. They brought it back to Mrs. Holroyd.

They told her the story about their trying to be detectives. Mrs. Holroyd was delighted to have the ring back. She said, "I want to say, 'Thank You' for being so clever, and being so honest, in bringing the ring back to me. I want to give you a Reward. The ring was a very valuable one, given to me by my husband, many years ago." She opened her handbag, and gave a five pound note each to each of the twins.

The Twins rushed home to their Mother. "What is a reward" they asked. Mother thought for a moment, and then she said, "A reward is someone's way of saying 'Thank You' for a special deed". The Twins understood.

If we do not say "Thank You" in life, we become ungrateful people. Other people do many good turns for each of us. Sometime, we give people a token Thank You, such as a bunch of flowers, or a box of chocolates. Another way of saying, "Thank You" to Sailors, Soldiers, and Airmen, is to give them a medal. When sports people compete in the World Games, representing their country, and they win, they receive a Gold, Silver, or Bronze Medal. Another way of saying, "Thank You", is to shake someone by the hand. When we want to thank God for his goodness to us, we say a prayer.

Prayer:

> It is good to give thanks unto God.
> Praise the Lord all his children.
> We thank you Father God,
> for the many people who work for us,
> without thought of thanks or reward.
> May we always appreciate their kindness.
> Teach us to be grateful.   Amen.

Hymn:

> Kum ba yah. (C&P.l. 68)

Teachers' Note: (1) To give a reward is a way of expressing our thanks for some good deed done for us. (2) There are very many people who work for us, without any thought of receiving either thanks or rewards. (3) To be grateful is the sign of good manners and good character.

(c) Thanking God!

When Jesus was passing through a village, ten men who were very ill with leprosy met him. Leprosy was a terrible skin disease, which gradually killed people. Lepers had to live apart from everyone else, in case they might infect others with the disease. Even when these men talked to Jesus, they had to stand at a distance. They shouted, "Jesus, Teacher, have pity on us!" Jesus looked at the ten lepers. He said to them, "Go show yourselves to the priests".

In Bible days, when anyone had been ill, and then had recovered from their sickness, they went to show themselves to the priest, in order to gain permission to live among healthy people again. As the ten lepers were going to meet the priests, on the way there, they were cured of their leprosy. Nine of the men went back home. One of the lepers realising that he had been healed, felt he needed to say "Thank you", to Jesus. This man was from a neighbouring country called Samaria.

The Samaritan returned to the village full of praises to God for his healing. He knelt at the feet of Jesus , and thanked him with all his heart. Jesus was very pleased that the man was genuinely thankful. Jesus said, "Were there not ten men who were cured, where are the other nine?" Then he spoke directly to the thankful man. "You may rise and go! Your faith has made you well."

It is always good manners to say "Thank You!" We ought to be thankful for everything which we receive. It is good when children include a "Thank you" to God in their prayers.

Now for a modern story. It was the day of the village Summer Fete. The Fete was a special day for everyone in the area. It was held on a lovely sunny day in the month of June. Everyone of importance was there. The local Councillors, the Doctor, the Nurse, the farmers, the Post-man, the school teachers, and the children from the village school, all met in Farmer Richard's field. The huge barn was close by. It could be very useful, to house the Fete, if it happened to rain. Everyone could be sure that they would not be wet.

There were stalls selling cakes, scones, and home-made biscuits. There were also vegetable and fruit stalls, craft stalls, games stalls, toy stalls, and a sweet-shop, selling ice cream. A group of Highland dancers performed dances. The brass band from the next village entertained everyone with music. Then the tea-time arrived. The tables were spread all over the farmyard. Some one shouted, "let us have the Vicar to say the Grace". Everyone looked around, but the Vicar had not attended the Fete. He had three churches to oversee, and he had completely forgotten about his duty at the Fete.

No-one attending the Fete that day wanted to say the grace. They were all rather shy about praying in public. What could they do? The school children from the village, whispered together. Suddenly, they all climbed up the steps of the wooden platform. Emma Walker, a girl aged twelve, spoke, "Let us bow our heads, and give thanks." The crowd became silent, and everyone kept very quiet. All the school children recited together, in perfect time.

"Thank you for the world so sweet.
Thank you for the food we eat.
Thank you for the birds that sing.
Thank you God for everything. Amen".

The children quietly came down from the platform, as if they were at the school Assembly. Farmer Richard, and the Local Councillors were very proud of their village children, because they knew how to give thanks to God for their food. Everyone enjoyed the meal. They never forgot the day that the Vicar forgot to come to the Village Fete.

Prayer:

Lord, we have so many good things in life;
food, and clothing, homes and friends;
health and strength.
May we never be unthankful.
Most of all we thank you for our perfect example,
Jesus Christ our Lord.   Amen.

Hymn:

When I needed a neighbour. (C&P.2. 65)

Teachers' Note: (1) The Bible story is found in St. Luke 17, verses 11-19. (1) Leprosy in these modern times can be cured by new medicines. (2) Lepers were very lonely people, because of their disease. This was the reason why ten of them kept together. They needed each other's company. (3) The point of the story is that everyone likes to have their prayers answered, but many forget to return their thanks to God.

(a) Will-Power

Lee was eleven years of age. He heard about the two-mile race round the Castle grounds. He expected some of the lads from the Junior School to be taking part, but when he asked the P.E. Teacher, he discovered that no-one from the school had entered the race. The Teacher said to Lee, "I would advise you not to enter this year, because there are a lot of older lads from the local Young Harriers Club taking part. They are lads highly trained at running the two miles. You might never complete the distance."

Nevertheless, Lee had set his heart on running the two miles. He began to train alone. For three weeks, each day, he would run two miles around the school sports field. At first he felt it to be a very long run. Gradually he became stronger. Lee was absolutely determined that he would at least run all the distance. His P.E. Teacher encouraged him.

The day of the race came round, and Lee went with his Dad to the castle grounds. There were many men there, who were experienced runners. Also, there were runners aged fourteen to eighteen. When Lee filled in the race entrance form, the organisers were surprised that Lee was only eleven years of age. They talked together, and decided to allow this determined boy to take part. All the runners lined up. The Starter gun was fired. The runners were off!

The Harriers were running very fast. Lee was at the rear of the runners from the start. He did not care about anything, except that he would complete the distance. The first mile was rather long, but fairly easy. Lee did not stop, but began to run the second mile. He felt a stitch in his side, as he quickened his pace.

Now an argument began in Lee's mind. "Should I not give up: I have run half the race? The other half seems so long, and my side is getting sore. No! I will not give up. I will complete the distance". By this time, many of the front runners had finished the race. Lee gritted his teeth in determination.

Lee had made up his mind, not to stop until he had reached the finishing point. His legs seemed to become heavier. He just kept them moving. As he came round the field towards the end, he heard a mighty roar from the huge crowd. He was last in the race, but no-one in the crowd moved, they were waiting and cheering for Lee. Lee felt very important now! Tears came down his face as he passed the finishing point. The crowd were cheering the brave boy, who had finished running the two mile race against the men, and the older boys. Lee was so excited, that he did not notice the television camera-men filming various parts of the race.

The winners received their prizes. Lee's Dad gave him a big hug. They went home in the car. Lee whispered, "Well, Dad, I completed the distance. Two miles is a very long race." Dad whispered to Lee, "I am proud of you!" That evening, the family were listening to the local television Sports programme.

After the football results, the local T.V. Commentator said, "I want to show you some film of the Charity Day two mile road race at the Castle Grounds". The T.V. showed the runners starting off, and the winners coming to the tape at the finish. Then to Lee's amazement, the Commentator said, "Now here is the bravest runner today, as he finishes. Millions of people will now be watching this lad, aged eleven, who has shown such tremendous will power. He never gave up until he had completed the whole distance." The film showed the cheering crowds, and Lee running past the finishing line.

The Commentator said, "We will be sending Lee one of our special yellow sports tee shirts, and a silver wrist watch. He was the bravest runner at the Castle today, because he never gave up." Lee quickly pedalled home on his bike every day, after school, to see whether the Postman had called. On the Thursday following the T.V. programme, sure enough, the parcel had arrived. In it were the yellow tee shirt, the watch, and a letter of congratulations. The Commentator wrote, "Lee, if at first you don't succeed; try, try, and try again!"

Prayer:

> Lord, forgive us if we begin some good deed,
> and then we give up half way through.
> Give us that inward determination,
> to complete our good deeds.
> Bless all sports people, runners, swimmers,
> footballers, and cricketers.
> Enable us to give of our best.   Amen.

Hymn:

> To ev'rything, turn. C&P.2. 113)

Teachers' Notes: (1) Many people begin well, but do not finish well. (2) It requires an inner kind of strength or "will-power" to reach our goals. (3) More people are watching and encouraging us than we ever realise.

(b) Kevin's Courage   *Week 4   Strength*

There is another unseen kind of power inside us, known as "Courage". Kevin had been knocked down on the road by a car. After spending some time in hospital, he was allowed to go home, on the condition that he kept to his wheel chair. He had to return to hospital at a later date for another operation on his leg. For this reason he was not allowed to walk. The Doctor wanted to allow time for his leg to grow a little, before the next operation. Kevin was a very brave boy. Although he hated having to sit in a wheel chair all the time. He knew it was for his own good.

Kevin was able to move the wheels of his chair with his hands. He had to be careful about not going too fast on the pavement. This constant use of his hands and arms made his muscles very strong. Having to sit in a wheel chair meant that Kevin could not play football, or any of the other fast moving games which children play. Yet Kevin never complained. He was glad to be alive, after his accident. He went to school with the other children, and they often pushed his wheel chair for him. The Teacher had reserved a special place in the class, for Kevin at a table with three of his friends. His wheel chair was stored in a corner of the class.

One Thursday afternoon, Kevin was going down the High Street, past the village Post Office, after school. He saw three men coming out of the Post Office carrying bags. They put the bags into the back seat of a large car, which was parked outside. Kevin was a member of the local Scout Troop. He had been taught to be observant. Kevin thought that something very strange was going on at the Post Office, because Thursday was early closing day, yet the door was open. It seemed strange that the three men were loading bags into a car, instead of into a red Post Office van. Kevin took out his pen, and he wrote the registration number of the car on the back of his hand.

Then with great effort, and perspiration pouring down his face, he pushed his wheel chair, turning the wheels as fast as he could. He made for the home of Mr. and Mrs. Barnfield. They were members of the Neighbourhood Watch Committee, who organised people in the street, to watch each other's houses, in case of burglars. Kevin breathlessly rang their door-bell and told Mr. Barnfield what he had seen, and gave him the car registration number written on the back of his hand. Mr. Barnfield, immediately rang for the Police, and told them what was happening.

The Police set up road blocks on the roads around the village. Soon the car, with the three men in it, was stopped at a road junction. The men were taken to the Police Station, and there they were questioned. Bags full of stolen Post Office property, valuables and money were found in the car. Kevin was correct, the men had robbed the Post Office.

The Chief of Police thanked Kevin for being so observant, and for showing such courage. He said, "Kevin, soon the Doctor will make your leg better. Soon you will get out of that wheel chair. Then, if you work hard at school, when you grow up, perhaps, you will become a Policeman. I notice four things about you Kevin. They all begin with the letter "C". You used your common-sense. You were clear in your message. You have courage. You were calm."

Next time you read the Ten Commandments, notice that the eighth commandment says, "Thou shalt not steal." Now, we understand much better what the commandment means. When you have courage, you may also experience fear. All brave people may feel afraid in an emergency, but their inner courage overcomes fear.

Prayer:

> Father God, give us all courage,
> to ever do what we know is right.
> Forgive us if we are moral cowards.
> We pray also for common-sense.
> May we never steal anyone's property.
> May we never spoil anyone's good name,
> by telling lies about them.   Amen.

Hymn:

> Lord make me a mountain standing tall for You. (JP. 421)

Teachers' Note: (1) Handicapped children are God's special children. We should always help them, when they cannot help themselves. At the same time, we must also treat them as they want to be treated - just like everyone else. (2) Courage is an inner strength which we all may possess. Most brave children know inward fear, but they show courage, by over-coming their fear. (3) The eighth commandment applies to robbers and to children alike. It reads, "Thou shalt not steal." (Exodus, Chapter 20. verse 15.)

(c) Samson the Strong Man   *Week 4   Strength*

The Israelites were troubled by the attacks of the Philistines who lived along the Mediterranean Sea coast. The Philistine army often marched into Israel and ruled the people very harshly. One day God sent a message to Manoah and his wife that they would have a baby son. This child was to be a Nazarite from the day he was born.

Being a Nazarite implied four things:

> First, he was not to drink any alcoholic drink, such as wine.
> Secondly, he was not to eat anything which was (ritually) unclean.
> Thirdly, he was never to have his hair cut.
> Fourthly, he was to be set apart for God's special service.

When the baby was born, they called him Samson. He never had his hair cut. This was a sign to people of Israel that Samson was God's special servant. As Samson grew up he became a very strong man. There were times when the Spirit of the Lord came upon Samson, and he became even more unusually strong. One day Samson was walking through the Vineyards, when a lion sprang out at him. Samson killed the lion with his bare hands. Yet he never told his parents about what he had done.

News of his great strength spread among the people. They told how Samson had set fire to the cornfields of the Philistines. They told a story of how he had killed a thousand Philistines with the jaw-bone of a dead ass. One evening the Philistines knew that Samson was in the town of Gaza. They secretly surrounded the place, and waited for the night to pass, so that they could kill Samson next morning, when it was day-light. They had locked the gates of the city securely, to keep him inside the city walls. During the night, Samson lifted in his arms, the gates, still attached to the gate-posts and carried them to the top of a hill.

Samson fell in love with a beautiful Philistine girl called Delilah. The Philistine Kings had promised Delilah eleven hundred silver coins if she could find the secret of Samson's strength. Delilah pleaded with Samson, "If you love me, then tell me the secret of your strength." Samson, teased her with wrong answers to her question. First he said, "Tie me up with seven new ropes, then I shall be weak." So Delilah tied him up with seven new ropes. Philistine soldiers were in hiding, ready to capture Samson. Delilah called out, "Samson, the Philistines are here!". Samson just snapped the seven ropes like breaking a thread. So Delilah had not found out the secret.

Another time she pleaded with Samson to tell her the secret of his strength. He told her to weave the seven locks of his hair into her weaving loom, then he would be weak. Samson went to sleep, and she wove the locks of his hair into her weaving loom. She called out that the Philistines were in the room, and Samson awoke, and jumped up, carrying Delilah's weaving loom along with him.

The third time, Delilah pleaded with Samson to tell her the secret of his strength. She asked him so often, that in the end, he told her the secret of his strength. "He said, "I am a Nazarite. My hair has never been cut in all my life. My strength comes from God.""

Later, Delilah, stroked Samson's head until he rested it upon her lap, and went fast asleep. Delilah had already betrayed Samson's secret to the Philistines. Delilah arranged for a man to cut off Samson's seven locks of hair, while he was sleeping. Then the Philistines rushed into the room. Samson arose angrily, but he found that his strength was gone. He was weak, just like any other person.

The Philistines took him away. They bound him in chains. Samson was blinded by the Philistines, and they put him into prison. His captors made him grind corn in the prison mill. The Philistines did not realise that Samson's hair had begun to grow again.

A large Feast was being held to honour the Philistine's god, Dagon. They brought Samson into Dagon's temple. They intended to make fun of Samson in his weakness, because he was their enemy. The Temple Feast was crowded with people, who had come to see the Philistines making fun of Samson. They placed Samson, standing in chains between the two pillars which held up the roof of the building. Samson prayed that God might give him his strength back again, just once more. Then he put his arms around the two pillars, and pulled them with all his might. The temple came crashing down killing everyone in the building. Samson was also killed that day, in his last show of strength. He killed more Philistines in his death, than he ever did in all his life-time.

Prayer:

> Lord, we all love to be strong.
> Let us not show our strength,
> by hurting other people.
> Let us rather use our strength,
> to help those who are younger,
> and weaker than we are.
> Make us strong and kind.   Amen.

Hymn:

> Be bold, be strong, for the Lord your God is with you. (JP. 14)

Teachers Note: The reference is found in Judges Chapters 13-16. In its biblical context it is beyond the understanding of the Primary School age. (1) Samson was brought up with a good religious family background. (2) It is sad that Samson had to spend his life fighting other people. (3) Consider how many ways children could use their strength to help others.

(a) The Old Violin

Monish and Pria were the children of Indian Parents. Their parents had come to England to work at the hospital. The two children were searching in the attic at the top of their house for a box of games they had played with when they were younger. They did not find the box of games, but they found an Indian musical instrument instead. It was shaped like a school recorder but much larger. First, Monish and then Pria tried to play notes on the Indian Pipe. They could not get much music out of the instrument. "I wonder if this is the kind of Pipe some

people play in India to charm snakes, and make them come out of a basket?",
Monish said. Pria brought the Musical Pipe downstairs to her mother. He mother
laughed to herself, and she began to play a little tune on the Indian Pipe.

"Mother, why can we not play any music?" they asked. Mother said that to
play any instrument, one needed skill and practice. She smiled and said, "Not
everyone born in Scotland can play the bagpipes!" The children realised that this
was true. Their mother told them that the only way to obtain skill in playing any
musical instrument was to practice regularly. The children decided to put the
Indian pipe back in the attic.

Their mother had brought out an old book from the bookcase. She said to the
children, "If you sit down, I will read you part of an old American poem which is
a story about musical skill." The children loved to hear a story, so they sat down
to listen to mother reading aloud. Before mother began to read, she told the
children that the poem was about a violin. Mother said that a violin was the one
musical instrument which came nearest to the sound of a human voice. When a
violin is played skillfully, it is sweeter than the song of any singing bird. She told
them that a violin could be played to imitate a bird song. Then Mother began to
read.....

The Touch of the Master's Hand.

> T'was battered and scarred, and the Auctioneer
> thought it hardly worth his while,
> to waste much time on the old violin,
> but he held it up with a smile.

> "What am I bidden Good Folk", he cried,
> "Who'll start the bidding for me.
> A dollar - a dollar, now who'll make it two,
> Two dollars, and who'll make it three.
> Three dollars once; three dollars twice;
> Going for three - but No!

> From the room far back, a grey haired man
> came forward, and picked up the bow.
> Then wiping the dust from the old violin,
> and tightening up the strings,
> he played a melody pure and sweet,
> as sweet as an angel sings.

> The music ceased, and the auctioneer
> in a voice that was quiet and low,
> said, "What am I bid for the old violin?"
> And he held it up with the bow.

> "A thousand dollars! Who'll make it two?
> Two thousand dollars. Who'll make it three?
> Three thousand once! Three thousand twice!
> And going, and gone! said he.
>
> The people cheered, but some of them cried,
> "We do not quite understand.
> What changed its worth? The man replied,
> "The touch of the Master's hand!"

Mother explained to Monish and Pria, that no one had realised that among the crowd in the auction room, there was an old man, who really was a brilliant violinist. The violin had not changed! It was the skill of the Master-musician's hands that was able to bring out the wonderful music.

The violin was now worth a thousand times more than it was before. People realised what beautiful music could be brought out of the old violin. As the poem says," He played a melody, pure and sweet; as sweet as an angel sings." Sometimes when we hear lovely music, we are lost for words to describe it! Mother became silent. Monish and Pria now understood a little more about music.

To play any instrument, first, we need talent, and secondly, we need daily practice. A famous musician once said, "If I do not practice for one day, I know it! If I do not practice for two days, my audience knows it! If I do not practice for a week, the world would know about it!"

Prayer:

> Father God, we thank you for the gift of music;
> for music in school, and in church;
> for music on the Radio, and on the Television;
> for Music that we love to hear;
> and for the world of music, we have yet to learn.
> Help us to use our talents.   Amen.

Hymn:

> Praise the Lord in everything. (C&P.l. 33)

Teachers' Note: The poem should be read extremely slowly. (1) Children love music. (2) Some children are very talented musicians, but even they need to practice in order to gain more skills. (3) Music has the power of bringing people together. (eg: Concerts, Hymns, or the National Anthem).

(b) Ian's Bugle.

Ian had one possession of which he was very proud. It was an old army bugle. How it came to be in the family ownership no-one really knew. Ian could not blow the bugle very well, because he did not have a Music Teacher. Ian knew the names of all the bugle calls: "reveille, assemble, charge, advance, rally, retreat, lights-out, last post, and call to arms". A friend had taught Ian to blow only one bugle-call. The problem was that Ian did not know the name of that particular bugle-call. However, he had caught the sound of the tune inside his mind. He loved to blow this call. When Ian blew the bugle, the children would sing;

"Come to the cook-house door boys. Come to the cook-house door! Dinner's ready, dinner's ready; Come to the cook-house door!"

Ian did not know whether the children were right or wrong in what they sang. He meant to learn to play the bugle properly some day.

The school were going on a walking trip across the moor. They arrived by coach at one side of the moor, and began their walk. The coach was to meet them on a country road on the other side of the moor. The children were wearing strong shoes, or walking boots, and each child carried a Cagoule, and a packed lunch. Ian had turned up with his bugle. A yellow rope was attached to the bugle, and slung across his shoulder. He would never allow anyone else to blow the bugle.

The moor was a vast area. Heather and bracken spread like a carpet for many square miles before them. There was not a house to be seen. Sheep and their lambs were grazing here and there. There were very few trees to to mark out the direction of the way they were walking..

The first two miles of the moor were easy to walk. It was a lovely Summer day. Then the wind changed, and blew across the moor. It was just a gentle wind, but it brought a damp mist over the moor. After the third mile it became very dense just like a fog. It was very difficult to see the path ahead.

The wind stopped, and the fog became so thick, that the group realised that they were lost on the moor, about two miles from the road. No one could see far ahead. They kept falling over sheep, which were walking about in the fog. One of the Teachers carried a mobile 'phone. He sent out a call for help to the Police. "We are lost on the moor, and we do not know where we are. We cannot see our path."

The Police Radio Operator replied, "We have Patrol Cars quite near. We will try to find you. There are good roads over the moors, but there is a swampy marsh not far from you. Stay still where you are. Repeat! Do not advance in the fog. Remain where you are!" The school party sat down in the grass, in the fog. It was rather warm. They talked for about half an hour, and ate their sandwiches. They were having a real adventure. Then they heard police car sirens very far away. They came nearer, and then they seemed to be far away again.

The children became anxious, as the two Teachers kept watch over the party. Then they heard more cars. They seemed to be about a mile away in the fog. The noise of cars stopped, and started, and stopped again. Ian thought to himself. "If I blow my bugle, and everyone sings, then the searchers will hear us. They will find us in the fog." The Teachers were pleased by Ian's suggestion. Ian blew his bugle loudly. The children sang;

Come to the cook-house door boys! Come to the cook-house door! Dinner's ready! Dinner's ready! Come to the cook-house door!

Two Police cars were searching the moor road, with their headlights turned on full. The Policemen were amazed to hear a bugle call, sounding over and over again. The gentle wind was carrying the sound for miles. The Police cars changed direction and made for the bugle sounds. Then they heard the children singing in the fog. At last the Police searchers and the lost children met together. The children were delighted to crowd into the Police cars, and get a ride back to their waiting coach. That evening, they had an exciting story to tell their parents about Ian and his bugle.

Next morning, at school, the Assembly lesson was about the Bible story of how the Israelite army marched round the city of Jericho. They marched once every day for six days. Then on the seventh day, they marched around the city seven times. When the Israelites blew their trumpets, the walls of Jericho fell down, and the Israelites captured Jericho. The Teacher explained that the trumpets, just like a bugle could be used in two ways. They were used to make music. They could also be used to send a signal. Good music entertains us, and carries a message. The Teachers and children turned round, looked, and smiled at Ian, and Ian grinned back at them!

Prayer:

> Lord, we thank you for all musical instruments,
> which bring happiness to our lives.
> We thank you for the Piano, and the Organ,
> used in school or in church.
> We thank you for bugles, and trumpets,
> which may be used to make either music, or a signal.   Amen.

Hymn:

> Joshua fit the battle of Jericho. (JP.143)

Teachers' Note: (1) Bugles and other musical instruments may be reproduced by an organ. (eg: Trumpet stop.) (2) The Scouts and Boys Brigade often have Bugle Bands which give pleasure to people. (3) Though the Bugle is a musical instrument, it may be used to send out a signal. eg: "Reveille" in the morning at school camp: "Last Post" on Remembrance Sunday. (Bugles are similar to shortened Trumpets, and often mentioned in the Bible.) The capture of Jericho is found in Joshua Chapter 6.

(c) David's Harp *Week 5   Music*

One day Samuel the Prophet of the Lord came to visit the home of Jesse in Bethlehem. He had been sent by God to anoint the next King of Israel. Saul the reigning King began as a good King, but he soon became very selfwilled.

Jesse had seven sons, and each son was very strong healthy. Samuel invited Jesse and his sons to a feast. When they arrived, Samuel spoke to each one of the seven sons, saying to himself, "Surely this man is the one who God has chosen to be king." However, each time God told Samuel by an inward voice, "No this is not the chosen one." God was urging Samuel not to choose from a man's outward good looks, but rather he was to choose for his good inward nature.

Samuel asked Jesse, "Have you any more sons?" Jesse, the father, answered, "Yes, I have another son, but he is the youngest. He is out in the fields looking after the sheep." Samuel insisted, " I must see him." Jesse sent for David his youngest son. Samuel, knew immediately in himself, "This is the next King." He took a horn of oil, and poured it over David's head, anointing him to be the future King of Israel. Then Samuel went home. David continued to watch over his father's sheep on the nearby hillsides.

King Saul became very moody. People thought that he was becoming mentally ill. They suggested that the King needed to hear music, to calm his nerves, and to help him to forget his troubles. Someone suggested that David the son of Jesse was good at playing the harp. The young David came to the Kings court. He played music for the King on his harp. It had a good effect on King Saul's mind. He improved. However, after David killed Goliath, by throwing a stone from a sling at him, everyone admired David. They thought that David was a hero. Saul in his moods, became very jealous of David.

One day, when David was playing his harp,Saul became jealous, and he picked up a spear, and threw it at David. The young musician quickly moved aside and the spear just missed him. David escaped from Saul's court. David gathered a band of men around him. They had to live like out-laws, among the hills, hiding from Saul. The King and his army pursued after him, and David had many narrow escapes.

Once, King Saul with his army made camp. Saul lay sleeping, with his spear stuck into the ground. David and two of his soldiers came in the darkness, slipping past Saul's guards. David's soldiers whispered to him, "Here is your chance, now! Kill Saul while you can!" David said, "I cannot harm the man whom God made King." Instead, they picked up Saul's spear, and his water jug. When they were on a hill, a safe distance from the camp, David and his men made a loud noise. It awakened all Saul's camp. David called out to Saul's guards. "Look, I have Saul's spear and water jug. You ought give better protection to your King." King Saul realised that David had spared his life the previous night.

Some time later, King Saul died. He had lost a battle with the Philistines, and rather than be captured, he fell on his own sword. So the shepherd boy who played the harp, and was anointed with oil by Samuel, became King in Saul's place.

David is remembered in history because he made Jerusalem the capital city of the kingdom. To this day, Jerusalem remains the capital. David was a King who was very much loved by his people. Some of the Psalms in the Bible were written by him. The Psalms are really another name for "Songs." The Hebrew people loved to sing David's Psalms, and to play their harps as they sang. Nowadays, modern Orchestras sometimes have harps. Wales, and in Ireland are famous for harp playing.

Prayer:

Father God, we thank you for the story
of the shepherd boy, who played the harp,
and became King David.
May we use our musical talents
for our own pleasure, and to give joy to others.
Teach us that in music we may also worship God.   Amen.

Hymn:

Only a boy called David. (JP. 190)

Teachers' Note: (1) David came from very humble beginnings. He was only a shepherd boy. (2) David loved God more than he loved music. (Not all the Psalms were written by David!) (3) David never took revenge on King Saul. He respected the man whom God, through Samuel, had previously anointed to be the first King of Israel.

(a) The Coconut

Geoff loved to read about fair-grounds,and when a travelling fair arrived in town, he immediately wanted to visit it. Geoff had watched the big fair-ground trucks and caravans being driven down the road towards the local playing fields. The fair-ground was about one mile away from his house. Geoff was nine years old, and had never visited a fair-ground before. His Dad had promised to take him to the fair-ground on the following Friday evening. Dad said that they both could enjoy all the fun of the fair together. Friday was yet three days off.

Geoff thought that three days was too long to have to wait. He wanted to go to the fair that very evening. Both his Dad and Mum said that he must wait until Friday. Geoff felt very bad tempered, so he stamped his feet in an angry tantrum. Mum told him not to be so foolish. She said that only little children behaved in such a childish manner. Yet Geoff still sulked, and began to cry. Finally, his mum had to send him up to his bedroom. She told him to stay there until he had cooled down, and become sensible again.

Geoff remained in the bedroom, sulking, until he became tired of being alone. He pushed up the bed-room window, and looked down on the flat roof of the garage. He thought to himself, "I could easily climb out the window, and walk along the roof of the garage, and climb down the spout. I could be on the ground and no-one would ever know." Then he did a very wrong thing. Geoff took the money out of his piggy bank, and put it in his pocket. He climbed out the window and ran off to the fair-ground.

He arrived at the fair. The Big Tent was there. The huge motor trailers were lined up in a circle. There were many stalls offering prizes for doing difficult things, such as knocking cups and plates off a shelf at the back of the stall. There was a man standing beside a machine. He was holding a huge rubber hammer. After people had paid their money, they were allowed three chances to hit the machine very hard with the rubber hammer. If the bell rang, then they received a prize. There were also, "roll a penny" stalls. Some stalls were selling candy floss and ice cream. There were one armed bandits full of money and prizes.

Geoff spent most of his money on the side-shows. At last he came to the Coconut Shy. He paid his money, and received six wooden balls to throw at the coconuts on a shelf at the back of the canvas stall. He threw the wooden balls with all his might, and managed to knock a coconut off the shelf. The lady in charge of the stall gave him the coconut as a prize. Geoff looked at his watch, and realised it was past his bedtime.

He ran all the way home. He knew that he could not climb up the spout, and cross the roof of the garage, to get back into his bedroom, where he was supposed to be. Instead, when he reached his own house again, he gently pushed the back door open. He was just climbing quietly on his tip-toes up the stairs, when his Mum and Dad came down the stairs. They had realised that he was missing from his bedroom.

Geoff confessed to his parents what he had done. He admitted he had taken his piggy-bank money, and that he had climbed out the window and spent most of the money at the fair-ground. Geoff was really a good boy, in spite of his bad temper. He never liked telling lies to his parents. Geoff had hidden the coconut inside his jacket. Slowly, he pulled out the coconut, and showed his prize to his parents. Dad and Mum said that they would forgive him this time, but he must never do such a foolish action again. They said that the garage roof was in need of repairs, and he might have fallen through it, and been badly hurt. There was also the danger of meeting harmful strangers at the fair.

Geoff wanted to eat the coconut. He quickly broke it open, but, inside the shell of the coconut, it was rotten and smelly. No-one would ever want to eat it.! Geoff realised that his prize was only a rotten coconut. He thought to himself, "This is a punishment for me. I have wasted all the money which I had saved in my piggy-bank, and I have nothing to show for all my efforts. Nothing, except a rotten coconut! How foolish I have been." From that time onwards, Geoff made up his mind to be obedient. He never deceived his parents again!

Prayer:

> Lord, teach us all to be obedient.
> Show us that many things are worth waiting for.
> May we never deceive out Parents.
> Help us to grow into young people,
> who can control our tempers, and never sulk.
> Lord, give us patience.
> Give us truthful speech and honest hearts.   Amen.

Hymn:

> Give us hope Lord. (C&P.2. 87)

Teachers' Note: (1). Obedience to Parents is wise. Patience is the ability to wait. Impatient children are not nice children to know. (2). We should never deceive our Parents because they love and care for us. (3). Often wrong actions bring their own punishment.

(b) Telling Lies

Week 6   Attitudes to Parents

Lucy and her sister, Lynne were both twins. They hoped to begin school next year. They lived in a large house with their parents, and their Granny. Their back garden had a very high wall around it. Lucy and Lynne had not yet grown tall enough to see over the wall to the house and garden next door. One sunny day, their mother came to them, and told them that both she and Granny were going out to the house next door for only fifteen minutes. They asked the two girls to promise that they would stay inside the house until they arrived back. The two girls promised to remain inside the house, and to play with their games.

Off went Mother and Granny to visit the house next door. Fifteen minutes seemed to be a long time for the two little girls to wait. They could hear a lot of people in the next garden. Lucy and Lynne wondered what was happening. Both girls forgot their promise to their mother. They opened the back door, and went out into their own garden. "I wonder what is the excitement over the wall", said Lucy. "I can hear a lot of people talking together".

Lynne asked Lucy to help her up the wall to have a quick look. However, the wall was too high for them to get a clear view. Lynne ran into the tool-shed, and brought out the wooden step-ladder used by their father, when he was picking the apples and plums from the trees. They placed the ladder against the wall, and both little girls climbed up the steps. They had a splendid view, and no-one noticed that they were looking over the wall.

The people in the next garden were wearing their best clothes. They were standing together in four rows. A little old man was bending his head forward, and looking into a black box on three legs. Lucy and Lynne wondered why everyone was smiling, and remaining so still. No one moved. All at once, the little old man said, "That will be all for today! Thank You, ladies.!" The ladies began to move about again across the lawn, talking among themselves, before they left for home.

Lucy and Lynne, quickly came down the ladder. They put it back in the tool-shed. Then, they went back into the house, to play with their games again. They had decided, that they would tell Mother and Granny, that they had remained inside their own house all the time. When the door-bell rang, Mother and Granny came back.

"I do hope that you two girls have been obedient", they said. "Yes", the twins answered. We did not go into the garden. We stayed in the house, playing with our games." Mother and Granny were pleased that they could trust their girls to be obedient. The twins thought to themselves that no-one would ever know that they had been in the back garden.

A week passed by, and Mum and Granny were sitting with the girls by the fireside. Their Father came home with his newspaper under his arm. He settled down in a big arm-chair, to enjoy a good long read of the day's news from the paper. All at once, he became very angry. He held up the Newspaper. There on the front page was a photograph of the Ladies from the Church. It was a photograph taken in the garden next door. Mother asked the twins, "Where were you last Thursday, when Granny and I were out for fifteen minutes?" The twins told a very big lie. "They said, "We never left the room, Mother."

Then, their Father held up his newspaper, to let them see the photograph. Sure enough, all the ladies were standing in four rows, with the wall behind them. It was a lovely photograph, but only one thing spoiled it. On the top of the wall, the photograph showed the twins looking over, and grinning at the ladies, behind their backs. So, the twins lies had been found out. Father was very cross. Lucy and Lynne were very sorry, and asked their Parents to forgive them for telling lies. Dad, and Mum, freely forgave them. Granny said, "Don't let this ever happen again!" The twins learnt that when anyone tells one lie, that it takes many more lies, to hide the first one. They tried not to tell any more lies.

Prayer:

> Lord of all truth, make us truthful.
> Teach us not to tell lies.
> Make us more like the Lord Jesus,
> who never told a lie.
> When we are alone, make us reliable.
> At home or in school,
> may we try to tell the truth, the whole truth,
> and nothing but the truth.   Amen.

Hymn:

> The Lord's Prayer. (C&P.l. 51)

Teachers' Note: (1) The Twins were on trust. People may put us on trust, and we must learn to be responsible for our own actions. (2) The Twins told lies. It is always easy to tell a lie, but lies may later be found out. (3). The Twins were forgiven by their Parents. We also need to ask God's forgiveness. This is why we pray in the Lord's Prayer, "Forgive us this day our trespasses".

(c) Absolom

Week 6   Attitudes to Parents

King David was the second King of Israel. He became king, after the death of King Saul. David is remembered as the King who made his headquarters at Jerusalem. The Hebrew people thought of him as a great and a good ruler. Yet all kings have some weakness in their character. King David was not good at teaching self-control to his sons.

One of King David's sons was named,"Absolom". Being a royal prince, Absolom was highly honoured by the people. He was a very handsome looking man. The one feature which distinguished him from others was his beautiful long hair. Yet Absolom was discontented. He wanted to be King instead of his father, David. Nevertheless, in spite of Absolom's rebellious nature, David loved his son very much.

Absolom secretly plotted against his father. When people came to complain about their taxes, or other problems, Absolom used to meet them at the gates of the city. He would smile, and speak to them in a pleasant manner. All the time he was trying to win their hearts, so that they would make him king. He would say, "If I were king, I would soon solve your problems for you." In this underhand way, Absolom made many friends, and gained support against his father, David.

After a time, Absolom became bolder. Even though David was the lawful and anointed King on the throne, Absolom arranged to have himself proclaimed as the king. Absolom had raised an army of supporters to fight King David's army. However, King David had a trusted friend who acted as a spy in Absolom's company. He was able to secretly report to King David, any plans for rebellion being made by Absolom.

Such was King David's love for his son, Absolom, that he overlooked and forgave his son's rebellion. David was now a very old man. His army Generals advised him to place the war under their command, and to keep himself out of danger. A living king was more helpful to the nation than a king who had been killed in battle. So King David remained at home.

King David was still very worried about his wayward son's safety. He instructed the three Generals in charge of his army, that they were to deal gently with Absolom. When the two armies met, there was a fierce battle. Many soldiers were killed, but King David's army defeated Absolom's army. Absolom's soldiers had to escape for their lives. Absolom, riding his mule, also escaped from the battlefield as fast as he could.

Absolom was making his escape, his mule galloped underneath an oak tree with low spreading branches. His long hair, trailing in the breeze, became entangled in the branches. As the mule went onwards, from underneath him, it left Absolom hanging by the hair from the tree. King David's soldiers soon found him, caught by his own hair. Against the King's orders, they killed Absolom with javelins and swords. They buried his body in the forest, under a great heap of stones.

When King David heard the news that Absolom had been killed after the battle, he could hardly bear to hear the sad news. He wept for his dead Son. The people heard him sobbing, and saying aloud, "Oh, my son Absolom. How I wish that I had died for you! Oh, Absolom, my son!" Instead of the day being a day of rejoicing for the victory gained, it became a day of mourning for the death of Absolom.

The lesson from this story is that young people who do wrong, can cause their parents a lot of worry, and perhaps, even make them shed tears. How often nowadays, we hear parents say, "my son or daughter is mixing with bad company, who are leading them into bad ways." Rebellion, nowadays, involves crime, vandalism, and disregard for other people.

Prayer:

> Lord, you are our Heavenly Father.
> Sometimes we may rebel against your will.
> Help us to know that when we do wrong,
> we are sinning against the King of Kings.
> We thank you, O Lord, that there is forgiveness,
> when we pray, and say that we are sorry.   Amen.

Hymn:

> I planted a seed. (C&P.2. 134)

Teachers' Note: The story is found in II Samuel Chapter 18. (1) Parents and children have a responsibility to each other. (2) Parents love their sons and daughters, and often worry about them. (3) Young people who have done wrong, need to ask God for forgiveness.

(a) Who is Right?

Week 7   Telling the Truth

Some people are very proud. They think that they know more than anyone else. Once there were three blind men who had an argument about who knew the most. Blind Jack said that because he had a good nose, and could smell out things better than anyone else, he must know the most. Blind Albert said that because he had the best ears, he was the wisest of the three. He said that he could hear a train coming five miles away. Blind Tom said that because he was the oldest in age, that he must know more than any of his two blind friends.

A Wise Man was passing by, and he heard the three of the blind men boasting to each other. He decided to teach them a lesson. The Wise Man went to the Zoo and asked for the loan of an elephant. The Zoo-Keeper agreed to lend him Eddie the elephant, as long as the Wise Man promised to bring it back.

The Wise Man invited the three blind men to come to the school play-ground to meet Eddie the elephant. Blind Jack, Blind Albert, and Blind Tom, all agreed to come. The Wise Man had also invited all the school children to attend. He asked them to decide which of the blind men was the wisest.

The Wise Man asked each of the three blind men to examine the elephant, and then to describe exactly what an elephant was like. The children liked the competition very much, and wondered who would be the wisest.

Blind Jack felt the elephant's trunk. He said, "An elephant is like a long hose-pipe." Blind Albert felt the elephant's four legs. He said, "An elephant is like four tree's growing together. Blind Tom felt the elephant's two big ears. He said, "An elephant is like two big wings hanging downwards."

The children laughed at the answers given by the three blind men. They said, "All three of you are wrong!" The reason the three blind men were wrong, was because they were only partly right. Then the Wise man asked the children what an elephant was like? All the children answered together, "An elephant is like an elephant!" The Wise Man said, "Children you are wiser than these three proud men, because you can see an elephant from every side." The Wise man took Eddie the elephant back to the Zoo Keeper. The three Blind men never boasted about how much they knew again!

Another day, a foolish boy and a girl were playing with two tins of paint. They had two colours, blue and yellow. They poured both the yellow and the blue paint into one paint pot, and threw the empty pot away. Then they mixed the paints together. They decided to write the colour of the paint on a label outside the paint-pot. The Boy argued that the paint was yellow and blue. The girl argued that the paint was blue and yellow. What colour should they both have written on the label? (Blue and yellow make Green).

Unless we know all the facts about anything, it is difficult to make a decision. If we only hear one side of an argument, then we may come to a wrong conclusion. Try this one!

Two little girls went to church one Sunday. When they came home for dinner, one little girl told her mother that the church was half empty. The second little girl told her mother that the church was half full. Which girl gave the correct account? (Both were correct, of course!).

We must not be boastful and think that we know more than others , when what we know may be only partly true. Indeed. two people who argue may BOTH be wrong. Better still, two people who argue may BOTH be right! Remember that having friends is better than having arguments.

Prayer:

    Lord, forgive us if we are boastful and proud.

    Before we make any final decisions,

    help us to try to see all sides of the truth.

    Teach us to listen and to learn from other people.

    Show us that sometimes it is better

    to lose an argument, and to keep a friend.   Amen.

Hymn:

    You can build a wall. (Break out). (C&P.2. 91)

Teachers' Note: (1) All Children argue. (2) Children must be learn. (3) Often arguments are not worth having anyway! Arguments are not always about reasoning a matter through, but about having one's own way. (foolish pride!)

(b) The Town Hall Clock   *Week 7   Telling the Truth*

The big Town Hall clock always told the truth. He always showed the perfectly correct time on his dial, high above the Main Street. Year in, and year out, for one hundred years, everyone in the town could be sure of one thing, they could depend on their Town Hall clock. Indeed, everyone fixed their own house clocks by the time shown on the Town Hall clock. It happened that the clock became a little bored with his work, and tired of the wheels inside him going round and round. "He said to himself, "What is the point of my two hands always pointing to the correct time? I think that tomorrow, I shall tell lies. I will run slowly, and make everyone in town a half an hour late".

Early next morning, everyone rose out of bed as usual, and made themselves ready for the day. Most people looked at the clock as they walked down the High Street. On the Town Hall clock, the hands showed it to be eight o'clock, when it was really half past eight. "This is fun", said the clock to himself. "I am going to see what happens in town when I tell lies". The Bank Manager, who worked in London took his time, walking to the Railway Station, thinking he was early. When he arrived at the station, he found that his train had left, half and hour before he had arrived. He was very angry.

The milk-man was late delivering the milk, and everybody was late for breakfast. The Postman was also late delivering his letters. The Headteacher always went to school an hour before school began. However, at nine o'clock in the morning, no children were in the playground, and no other teachers had arrived at the school. The Headteacher wondered if everyone had the 'flu and whether they all had decided to stay at home. Of course, children and teachers arrived a half an hour late for school.

The Doctor was late for his patients in the Surgery. The Church Sexton rang the church bells for a wedding at the wrong time. The Post Mistress wondered why the Pensioners who usually queued outside the Post Office for their pension money, were not there. No-one had their morning coffee at eleven o'clock that day. The factory workers had to work a half an hour extra, because they arrived a half an hour behind time for their work. Everyone who believed the time on the Town Hall clock that day, found themselves to be half an hour late.

That evening, the people of the town held a meeting at the Town Hall. They said that they would never believe the clock again. No one ever mentioned that the old clock had told the truth for one hundred years. Everyone remembered the one day when the clock told lies about the time. The people voted that everyone in town ought now to buy a wrist-watch, and so they did!

The clock-mender climbed up his ladder and washed the clock dial. He oiled and cleaned it on the inside, and once more, the clock told the correct time. However, by this time, everyone had bought wrist-watches for themselves, even the school children. Sad to say, but no-one ever bothered to trust the Town Hall clock again. The towns-people used to say, "One bitten, twice shy." Everyone in future checked the the time on their wrist watches by the time given on the Radio. They forgot that they ever had a Town clock!

Have you noticed that when people tell lies, a similar thing happens. People, after a while, take no notice of what anyone who tells lies has to say. They can no longer be trusted.

Prayer:

>Lord, we thank you for people who tell the truth.
>Help us never to tell lies.
>Make us reliable in what we say.
>Make us more like our Lord Jesus,
>the one who never told lies.
>If we are tempted to be false,
>grant us your strength to be truthful.   Amen.

Hymn:

>God who made the earth. (C&P.l. 10)

Teachers' Note: (1) The Town Hall clock had a good record of telling the correct time. (2) Lies deceive and inconvenience everyone connected with them. (3) People do not usually trust people who tell lies.

168

(c) **Preaching the Truth** *Week 7 Telling the Truth*

The Lord spoke to Jonah one of his prophets, and told him to go to the city of Ninevah and preach to the people there, because they were a very wicked people. Jonah did not want to go. He believed that God was only the local God of his own land. So he decided to run away from God. He went down to the town of Joppa, which had a harbour. He found a ship sailing for Tarshish, which was in the opposite direction from Ninevah.

After he had paid his fare for the passage, he went down into the ship, and fell fast asleep. The ship set sail, and when far out to sea, a violent storm arose. The sea was so rough, that the ship was in danger of shipwreck. The sailors were afraid. Each man prayed to his god. They took the cargo, and threw it over-board to make the ship lighter, and higher in the water. Yet the storm seemed to get worse.

The ship's Captain found Jonah asleep down below deck. He awoke Jonah, saying to him, "You had better pray to your God, and it may be that he will save us from perishing in this terrible storm". The sailors decided to draw lots to find out who caused the storm. (They each one drew out straws from many straws tied together.) Jonah pulled out the only short straw. The sailors asked Jonah who he was? Where did he come from?

Jonah told him that he was a Hebrew, and that he worshipped the Lord, who had made the sea and the dry land. Jonah admitted that he had been disobeying the Lord, and that he was trying to run away from him. The sailors said to Jonah, "Tell us what to do to calm this violent storm?" Jonah told the sailors to throw him over-board, and the storm would become calm. The sailors really did not want to throw Jonah over-board and be responsible for an innocent man's death. They rowed even harder, but the storm increased. In the end, they took Jonah, and threw him over-board. They then worshipped Jonah's God.

The Lord had prepared a great fish to swallow Jonah. Time passed, and Jonah was in the stomach of the fish three days and three nights. Jonah prayed to the Lord inside the fish. The Lord caused the fish to spit Jonah out on the shore.

The Lord spoke to Jonah the second time, and commanded Jonah to go and preach to the city of Ninevah. This time Jonah obey the Lord. He went to Ninevah, and told the people, that unless they gave up their wicked ways, Ninevah would be destroyed in forty day's time.

The people believed the truth of Lord's message contained in the preaching of Jonah. Everyone, from the King of Ninevah downwards, dressed themselves in sack-cloth, and they put ashes on their heads. This was their way of showing that they were sorry, and that they had become humble before the Lord. They held a national fast, and no-one ate any food, to show the Lord how sincere they had become. The Lord changed his mind, because the people of Ninevah had payed attention to the preaching of Jonah. He did not destroy the city of Ninevah after all. Jonah by obeying the Lord, had saved all the people from certain destruction.

Prayer:

> Father God, we thank you for Lord's Ministers,
> who have preached the Gospel down the years.
> We thank you for preachers such as Jonah and Jesus.
> We thank you for all the people,
> who have shown us the ways of goodness.
> May we all obey you, our Father God,
> and walk the paths of peace.   Amen.

Hymn:

> I listen and I listen. (C&P.1. 60)

Teachers' Note: (1). Jonah was a disobedient prophet. We can never run away from God, because God is in us. (2). Jonah received a second chance. Not everyone gets a second chance. If we do get a second opportunity to do a good action, we should take it. (3). Jonah was inside the fish's stomach for three days and three nights. The early writers of the New Testament, believed that the Jonah story illustrated Jesus being in the Tomb for three days and three nights. (See Matthew 12:40.).

(a) A Woman Against the Wind   *Week 8   The Mighty Wind*

It happened more than one hundred years ago, in the days when sailing ships could still be seen around our coasts. All that week it had been stormy and cold. The Winter wind howled around the little farm house on a rocky sea coast. The farmer's wife had cared for her good husband and family all day long. Now, she was tired. She retired to bed. However, for some strange reason, she could not sleep.

The farmer's wife tried to imagine sheep going over a gate, and tried to count them as they went over. She thought that this was a good way to fall into a deep sleep. This time it did not work. She still lay awake. She heard the old clock in the next room strike the hour of twelve. She began to think about the number twelve.

She remembered that in the Bible, Jacob had twelve sons. There were the also the twelve tribes of Israel. There were twelve disciples. There were twelve months in the year. She knew that long ago there were the twelve signs of the Zodiac. She knew that there were twelve figures on a clock dial. She knew, (that in those days) there were twelve pennies in a shilling. She knew that a dozen eggs meant twelve eggs. After a short time she fell fast asleep.

She had a strange dream. She dreamt that an old beggar woman called at her cottage door. The old woman was hungry, and cold. The farmer's wife having a kind nature, gave her some food, and a bowl of hot soup to make her feel warm inside. In the dream, the old lady said to her. " You are worth twelve strong men. Never forget that! Promise me that you will never forget my words."

The farmer's wife promised never to forget the old woman's words. She slept soundly all night. Next morning she remembered her strange dream, and the old woman's words. "You are worth twelve strong men".

All that week it rained heavily, and the wind blew. The farmer had gone off to the market in town. His wife took a walk along the shore, to watch the waves come crashing on the rocks. As she walked, she saw a sailing ship struggling against the tide and the force of the wind. She saw the ship eventually being washed against the rocks. It was being broken to pieces by the force of the gale. It was a lonely stretch of the coast and no-one else was around. The farmer's wife realised that she must do something to help. Some of the men on deck secured a line tied to the ship's mast. Next, They threw the long rope to her. The force of the wind carried the rope towards the shore. The Farmer's wife caught hold of it.

What could she do? There were no trees at that place to which she could attach the rope. There were no fences. There was absolutely nothing to make the rope fast. There was no-one to help. She was alone. Without hesitating, the farmer's wife tied the rope around her own waist. She dug her heels into the sand, and pulled with all her might, making the line taut.

She could feel that every movement of the ship pulled at the rope. She prayed to God,"Lord give me strength." One by one the ship-wrecked seamen held on to the line, and entered the water, making for the shore. As the seamen reached the safety of the shore, they helped her hold the rope against the pull of the wrecked ship, which was moving about in the wind. She counted the crew as the men came ashore wet and bedraggled. There were twelve members of the crew, and all had been saved from drowning. The rescued sailors thanked her for saving their lives by holding the rope. Suddenly, she remembered the old woman's words in her dream. "You are worth twelve men!" Now she understood what her dream meant.

She guided the men along the windy shore to her little cottage, with its warm fire-side. Soon inside, she made a splendid hot meal for the sailors. The Captain, before eating, bowed his head, and said grace. "For what we are about to receive, may the Lord make us truly thankful." They were genuinely relieved to be safe and sound on shore.

The farmer arrived home from market, and was surprised to see twelve wet sailors sitting, having a meal in his farm-house. When he heard how his wife rescued the whole crew from the ship, he gave her a big hug. He said that he was the proudest husband in all the world!

Prayer:

> Father God, we ask you to bless all those,
> who sail the sea in ships.
> Guard them, and bless their wives and families,
> until they come home safely again.
> We pray for fishermen, and men on the oil rigs.
> Bless the brave Life-boat crews.   Amen.

Hymn:

> Spirit of God. (C&P.l. 63)

Teachers' Note: (1) This was a very brave and resourceful woman. (2) Sailors often risk danger, and are away from home for long periods. Some of the men whom Jesus chose as his disciples were fisher-men. (3) We should remember to pray for the brave Life-boat men, who are often in danger.

(b) Jonathan's Kite

Week 8   The Mighty Wind

It was a windy day in a West African village. The people lived in thatched huts in the forest. The Government engineers had bored two new wells for the people at the end of the village street. Previously, the people had to walk to the river to fill their water pots. Now, all they had to do was to pump the handle, and water poured out. Anyone in the village could come and take water from the deep well.

Jonathan occasionally went to school at the mission station. He was a boy who looked after his father's cattle, in case they strayed too near the large river, and were eaten by the crocodiles. He was a bright lad, and very intelligent, even though he had not spent much time in school.

The Government engineers returned to the village. They were now to build a steel bridge across the river. The steel wires, cables and iron girders had arrived by motor trucks from the coast. Jonathan the cattle boy watched with great interest, as the engineers unloaded the trucks of the building materials. It was a hot day, and the engineers shared their lunch with Jonathan.

Next week the engineers began their task of building the new bridge over the river. They intended to stretch great steel cables across the river, and then to attach steel girders to them. Finally, they intended to build a road on top of the girders. Everyone then could safely drive their cattle across the river, without any danger from the crocodiles.

The engineers had a problem. How could they get the great steel cables across the wide river, to the other engineers on the far bank of the river. One engineer had a good idea. He took a bow and arrow, tied string to the arrow. He shot the arrow across the water. However the river was too wide, and the arrows always fell short into the river. What could they do? They had no boat with them, and even so, the river was flowing too fast anyway.

The engineers held a meeting together. They talked a lot, but no one came up with an answer to the problem. Jonathan, the cattle boy heard them talking. He came into the engineers hut, and said to the engineers, "I could show you how to get the first rope across the river." At first they laughed at a the idea of a native cattle boy trying to teach the engineers. Then the Chief engineer became serious. He said, "Allow Jonathan to speak to us."

Jonathan said, "Last Christmas I was given a kite. If you tie light thread to my kite, I will let the wind carry my kite high up into the sky, until it reaches over to the other bank of the river. I can then lower the kite, until it is over the heads of the engineers on the other bank. Then they can stretch up, and take hold of the light thread, and remove it from the kite. I then will pull my kite back over the river again.

"What use is a light piece of thread," asked one of the engineers? "We have to get heavy steel cables across." Jonathan smiled at the engineers. He said, "The next thing to do, is to tie a piece of strong string to the thread, and the engineers on the other side will pull the strong string across." Jonathan went on speaking. "After that, if you tie a rope on to the strong string, they will be able to pull the rope across the river. Then, if you tie a steel cable to the rope, the engineers on the other side can pull the steel cable across.

With a steel cable across, you can pull anything else across, since the cable is so strong". The engineers were astonished at Jonathan's ideas.

Jonathan ran home for his kite. He brought it back to the riverside. They tied the first thread to Jonathan's kite, and the kite went high up into the sky. Jonathan lowered it over the heads of the engineers on the opposite bank. They carefully took hold of the thread. The whole process had begun. Soon the bridge-builders were building the steel bridge.

When the bridge was completed, the engineer held a little ceremony to open the new bridge for the people to use. A white silk ribbon was fixed across the opening, and Jonathan was given a pair of scissors to cut the ribbon, and declare the new bridge open. A freshly painted sign was on the bridge. Jonathan could not read, so he asked the Chief engineer to read the sign for him. To the boy's surprise, the sign read, "Jonathan's Bridge." Jonathan laughed to himself, and said to the engineers, "Do not thank me, thank the wind instead! "

Prayer:

> Father God, we thank you for the winds that blow,
> bringing rain to dry countries,
> and drying up the lands where the soil is too wet.
> We thank you for the breezes which blow,
> the sails of many boats at sea.
> We thank you for wind-mills creating power;
> for the winds that blow away the fog and smoke.   Amen.

Hymn:

> The Building Song. (C&P.l. 61)

Teachers' Note: (1) Water and winds are necessary for the existence of human beings on earth. (2) Jonathan did not have a full education at school, yet he knew about the usefulness of the wind. (3) Young people may help older people to see life from another view-point.

(c) The East Wind and the Red Sea   *Week 8   The Mighty Wind*

The Hebrew people had been slaves in Egypt. They were forced to make bricks from the clay, for the many buildings in Egypt. Pharaoh, the King of Egypt had set task-masters over the Hebrew slaves. These masters often used their whips to make the Hebrew slaves work harder. Pharaoh would not allow the Hebrew people to leave the country. The two Hebrew Leaders were Moses and Aaron. They pleaded before Pharaoh, that he should let the Hebrew people go free.

The Lord sent ten plagues upon the Egyptians. First, the water of the River Nile turned a red colour, and no one could drink it. Then there was a plague of frogs, followed by a plague of lice. Next, a plague of flies; a plague upon the Egyptian cattle; a plague of sores upon man and beast; a plague of hail and fire; a plague of locusts ate up every tree and plant; and a plague of darkness. Each time, Pharaoh promised to let the Hebrew slaves go free. Then, when the plague had passed away, he changed his mind again.

Last of all, the Lord sent the plague of death upon the first-born child in every house in Egypt. Moses had told the Hebrews to kill a lamb, and to sprinkle the blood upon the door-posts and the lintel of each Hebrew house. They were to make a special meal, and eat it dressed as if ready to go on a journey. When death passed over the land of Egypt that night, the first born child in every Egyptian house died, but none of the Hebrew first-born children were harmed.

Pharaoh, hearing that the Lord had struck down the eldest child in every Egyptian house, fearing worse plagues might happen, he gave permission for the Hebrews to leave. That night, all the Hebrew slaves, men, women and children escaped in the darkness. Six hundred thousand people marched in a great long line towards the Red Sea. (The Hebrews had been living in Egypt for four hundred and thirty years).

During the day, a pillar of cloud went before them to show them the way. At night a pillar of fire shone, so the Hebrews travelled both by day and by night. Pharaoh again changed his mind. He raised a large army to pursue the escaping Hebrew people. The pillar of cloud by day, and the pillar of fire by night,moved from before the Hebrews, to behind them. They were always between the Hebrews and the pursuing Egyptian army.

When the Hebrews reached the shore of the the Red Sea, the people were afraid. They were caught between the Sea before them, and the Egyptian army behind them. The people grumbled at Moses. "Do not be afraid, stand still, and see how the Lord will save you," said Moses. Then Moses stretched out his hand over the Red sea, and the Lord caused a strong East wind to blow back the waters of the sea, all through the night.

Next morning, the sea was divided, and the Hebrew people walked through the sea on dry land. They soon reached the other side. Then, the Egyptian army arrived. The horses and chariots, and the soldiers followed into the middle of the sea after the Hebrews. The wheels of the chariots began to stick in the wet sand. Moses raised his hand over the sea, and the tide changed. The rushing waters returned, and covered the Egyptian horsemen and their chariots. They were all drowned. When the Hebrew people on the other shore saw that their enemies had been destroyed, they sang a song of praise unto the Lord. Miriam, the sister of Moses, and the women, took tambourines and danced for joy, because for the first time in four hundred years, the Hebrew people were free. They travelled onward to the Promised land.

Prayer:

> Father God, we thank you for the story,
> of the Exodus of the Hebrew people.
> We thank you for everyone who has worked,
> to set people free from slavery.
> We pray that people all over the world,
> may help each other to be free.   Amen.

Hymn:

> When Israel was in Egypt's land. (JP. 276)

Teachers' Note: The Jewish and Christian religion might not have existed, if the Hebrews had remained slaves in Egypt. It marks a very important event in the history of the Hebrew people. (Just as the defeat of the Spanish Armada in a storm, marks an important event in British history.) (1). Slavery was once common. We should thank God for our freedom. (2) Moses and Aaron were good leaders, because they had faith in God. (3) People are happy when they are free. (This story may be found in Exodus Chapter 12.)

(a) The Ghost   *Week 9   In the Darkness*

During the Second World War, there were many air raids over British towns. Enemy aircraft dropped high explosive and incendiary bombs on the factories and streets down below. Thousands of children, families, and whole schools were evacuated from dangerous cities and towns to safe country areas. These town children were known as "Evacuees". They were billeted out in villages and farms among kind people who were willing to take them for the duration of the war. Usually, the children's parents had to remain in the towns to help with the war work at the factories. Many parents joined the armed forces (Army, Navy, or Air Force).

Once, there were seven evacuee children billeted on one farm in beautiful countryside. Many of the children from the town had never really seen the cattle grazing in the meadow, or the horses pulling the ploughs. (In those days there were not many tractors to be seen on the farms.) The children enjoyed walking through the farmyards, which were full of free range hens, geese, and turkeys pecking the ground for food. Many farms had their own duck ponds, or dove cotes. It was usual to have a small orchard behind the farmhouse.

The country children soon taught the evacuees the names of the trees and wild flowers all around them. The evacuees enjoyed helping the farmers to bring in the corn, wheat, and barley at harvest time. Later on, in September, many country schools shut down for a fortnight, to allow the children to help with the potato harvest.

The seven evacuee children enjoyed their stay on the farm. There was no electric light. Oil lamps were used to give light in the evenings. There was no gas in the country in those days, so most of the food was cooked in the farm kitchens on large coal and log fires. Bread was baked in the oven in the kitchen range.

One dark night the seven evacuees went upstairs to bed. The beds were in the three huge bedrooms. The bedrooms had doors adjoining each room, so that it was possible to pass through one room to another. At night some of the windows on the landing were always kept open, to allow fresh air to enter the rooms. The evacuees turned out their oil lamps and fell fast asleep. That night it was rather windy.

In the middle of the night, the children were awakened by a rustling sound, as if someone was outside, moving up and down the landing. All the evacuees were wakened by the frightening noise. They called to each other in the darkness, "Can you hear it?" Of course, everyone could hear it! Now it became a swishing sound, moving along the landing. Someone called out in the darkness, "It's a ghost!" All the children put their heads under the blankets. They were terribly frightened.

They kept still, but the rustling noise only moved away for a little while, and then it always came back again. Two of the bigger boys jumped out of bed, and all the others followed them. They decided to open only one of the doors, to get a good look at the ghost.

As the sweeping rustling noise came nearer, and nearer,they opened the door and looked up the landing. The moon was shining in the window. They could see that a large newspaper had been blown open by the wind. Each gust blew the pages rustling around on the landing. It was the movement of the paper which caused the noise.

The children laughed in the darkness. One of the older boys said, "It's not a ghost after all, it is only a newspaper blown by the wind." The farmer sleeping downstairs, hearing the noise of feet upstairs, came up to see what was the matter. He carried his oil storm-lantern in his hand. When he heard what had happened, he also just laughed. He said, "I must have forgotten, and left that newspaper on the chair at the top of the landing last night."

The evacuees all climbed back into their beds. The Farmer smiled at them and he said, " It is like a hunter being afraid of a paper tiger. There is no such thing as a ghost! If you say your prayers at night, then God will take care of you! Imagine being afraid of a newspaper! Good night everyone. God bless you!" Everyone fell fast asleep. The evacuees were never afraid of ghosts again. However, before going to bed, they always made sure that no newspapers were left near an open window again.

Prayer:

> Father God, we thank you for the night time.
> Teach us never to be afraid of the dark,
> because God is always near us.
> We thank you for rest and for sleep,
> which refreshes us for a new day.
> Bless sick people who find it hard to sleep.
> Give them your peace of mind, we pray.   Amen.

Hymn:

> Sad, puzzled eyes. (C&P.2. 74)

Teachers Note: (1) The countryside can be a wonderful place to learn about nature. (2) We ought to be thankful for the miracle of sleep. We wake up refreshed and ready for a new day. (3) There is never any need to be afraid of the dark, because God is always near us.

(b) The Boy with the Bright Idea   *Week 9   In the Darkness*

It was a small American town. The town had a good College with a large sports field. Most people in the town were proud of their College, and of the young people who attended it. That night the Head of the Police was on night duty at the police headquarters. Late that evening, he had an emergency call from the operations room at a large airport, one hundred miles away.

The Flight Planners at the airport, spoke over the Radio Telephone. "Hello, Chief of Police. We have an emergency on our hands. Please, listen carefully. A small aeroplane cannot make it back to the airport here. They have lost their directions, and worse still, the aircraft is running out of fuel. They will have to make a forced landing very soon. We have calculated that in half an hour they will be over your town. Can you help to guide this aircraft down to a safe landing place in the darkness. I am sorry, but that is all I can tell you just now!"

The Head of Police was just about to call out the emergency services, when he realised that he did not know what to do in this situation. They had never planned for such an emergency. Just then, Gerry, his twelve year old son called in to see him. Gerry had been on his way home from the the Scouts that evening. "Sorry, Gerry", he said, "I have an emergency on my hands, and I don't know how to deal with it. An aircraft is going to crash land on the town."

Gerry was an intelligent boy. "Dad, he shouted, use the College sports ground. It is very large and level". The Chief of Police answered Gerry. "I had already thought of doing that myself. The aircraft will never see the sports field in the darkness." It was then that Gerry had a bright idea. "Dad, telephone the local Radio Station quickly, and ask the Announcer to tell everyone about the emergency. Ask volunteers to bring their cars to the College Sports Ground immediately." The Chief of Police thought Gerry's idea was a brilliant one!

Quickly, he telephoned the Announcer at the Radio Station. The Announcer first made sure that it was not a joke, and that it really was an emergency. Then, over the Radio, he asked for cars to come to the College sports field immediately. Meanwhile, the Chief of police had called out the emergency services, Fire, Ambulances, and Police Squad cars to the College sports field.

A large number of cars arrived. They were told to quickly line up in two straight lines on the College field. One line was ordered to face the other line, turn on their head-lights, and to keep their engines running. As the drone of an aircraft engine was heard in the darkness of the black sky, there on the College field were two lines of lights, just like an airport landing field. Behind them were the emergency services.

The aircraft had used up almost all its fuel, and the Pilot was desperately looking for somewhere to crash land. He was surprised to see the lights of a landing strip under him. He gently guided his aircraft downwards on to the sports field, and made a perfect landing. The engine was spluttering, as the fuel was almost finished.

The Pilot jumped out of his aircraft on to the ground. He carefully helped the other passengers out. Everyone was happy because passengers and crew had been saved from an air accident. The Pilot thanked the Chief of Police for alerting the town's emergency services. He thanked the car owners for their guiding headlights on such a dark night. The Chief of Police said to the Pilot, "There is someone else you must thank. We only acted on his bright idea!" The Pilot thanked Gerry, for his presence of mind. Later, Gerry was awarded a medal from the Police Department.

Let us ask the question! Who really saved the aircraft? Was it the Chief of Police? Was it the airport Flight Planners who first telephoned? Was it Gerry with his bright idea? Was it the motorists who used their headlights to light-up landing field? Was it the Pilot who skillfully guided the plane down to safety? Was it the College Caretaker who opened the College gates in the darkness to allow the cars and emergency vehicles to enter?

The answer to our question is that everyone quickly working together saved the aircraft from crashing in the darkness. Everyone played a part in the emergency. We sometimes say, "Many hands make light work, but too many cooks spoil the broth."

Prayer:

> Lord God, we thank you for our modern age,
> when aircraft may help us to travel farther.
> We thank you for the emergency services,
> who are always on stand-by duty.
> Bless all passengers and crew on aircraft.
> Guard them in times of danger.   Amen.

Hymn:

> Autumn Days. (C&P.l. 4)

Teachers' Note: (1). Emergencies happen everyday somewhere. We need dependable emergency officials. (2). Gerry's quick thinking helped the Chief of Police. Young people's ideas are often very useful to adults. (3). It needs everyone working together to help in an emergency.

(c) Singing in the Dark   *Week 9   In the Darkness*

Paul and Silas were early Christian evangelists. They travelled together from town to town, opening new churches among those who believed in Jesus. When they reached Philippi, there was a slave girl who was possessed by an evil spirit. Her owners used her to tell people's fortunes. She earned her Masters much money. The slave girl followed Paul and Silas, shouting out, "These men are the servants of the supreme God". She did this day after day. Paul could not stand it any more. So he commanded the evil spirit in the slave girl, saying, "I command you in the name of Jesus Christ to come out of her." The evil spirit left the girl in peace.

The owners of the slave girl realised that they would not make any more money out of their slave. They seized Paul and Silas, and took them to the Magistrates. The slave Owners accused Paul and Silas of causing a disturbance in the city. The Magistrates arrested Paul and Silas. They were condemned. and flogged. This was contrary to Roman law, because Paul was a Roman citizen, as well as being a Jew. This meant that he had special Roman rights. The Philippian Magistrates did not realise this, before they had flogged the two Christians. Paul and Silas were then locked up in prison.

In the cell, at midnight, Paul and Silas were praying to God, and singing hymns in the dark. The terrible beating they had received caused them so much pain, that they could not go to sleep. Suddenly, in the middle of the night, an earthquake shook the prison, and the prison doors were opened. The prisoners chains fell off. The Jailor awoke out of his sleep, and seeing the prison doors open, he thought that the prisoners had escaped. He drew out his sword, and was just about to kill himself, because death was the Roman penalty for allowing prisoners to escape.

Paul called out in the darkness, "Do not harm yourself, we are all here."

The Jailor called for a light, and entered the cell. He was full of fear. Paul said to him, "If you believe in Jesus you will be saved." Paul and Silas talked to the Jailor about the teaching of Jesus. The Jailor became a Christian. He bathed the prisoners wounds, which had been caused by the whipping they had received. Immediately after that, the Jailor and all his family were baptised, as a sign that they all were now Christians.

The Jailor brought Paul and Silas to his own house. He provided good food for them. The Philippian Magistrates having found out that Paul was a Roman citizen, with special rights, they realised that they should not have condemned the two men to be flogged. As Magistrates, they themselves had broken the Roman Law. Now they were afraid for themselves. They sent word to Paul that they should leave the city in secret.

Paul refused to leave in secret. He told the magistrates that they had been openly condemned before everyone. Therefore, the magistrates must openly come, and set them free before everyone. The Magistrates came to the prison, and openly set Paul and Silas free. They asked them to leave the city.

Prayer:

> Heavenly Father, we are thankful,
> for the brave Christians of the past,
> who were willing to suffer for their faith.
> Help us also to be brave,
> As we try to be Christians, in this modern age.
> May we always be kind to others at school.
> Through Jesus Christ our Lord.   Amen.

Hymn:

> On the road to Damascus. (JP. 442)

Teachers' Note: (1) Paul and Silas were travelling Christian Evangelists. (2) Churches in the New Testament were not buildings, but rather groups of people, often meeting in houses. Church buildings came later. (3) Paul and Silas were willing to suffer for their faith. (The story is taken from Acts of the Apostles, Chapter 16. verses 16-40).

(a) The Miner's Lamp

This is a story from a mining community, as it used to be years ago. Jason's Father was a coal miner in County Durham. The family at that time lived in a small miner's cottage. Father had placed an old coal-miner's oil lamp on top of the kitchen dresser. There it stayed for many years. "When I die", said Father, "then Jason may have my lamp." Jason did not want his father to die, so he never thought about the lamp. The lamp was part of the kitchen decoration.

Years before, when Father was a younger man, he used to come home from the coal mine, as black as the coal itself. After working long hours in a coal mine, the workers were dirty from coal dust and grime. Every miner's home in the old days had a large tin bath. When the siren blew at the pit, indicating the end of the work shift, the miner's wives would have the water heated, and ready to pour out into the tin bath in the kitchen. Then Father would arrive home, and everyone left the room, until Father had his daily bath, in front of a warm coal fire. As soon as he was clean and fresh again, he was ready for his meal.

Two wonderful things happened at much the same time. First, Jason's family moved into a lovely new house, with its own bathroom. Then the Pit Manager announced that the Coal Board would be installing pit-head baths. This meant that all the miners could have hot and cold showers before they came home from work. The family discarded the old tin bath, but they still kept the Miner's lamp on the kitchen dresser. Jason was pleased to see his Father come home after work, no longer black with coal dust, but as clean as he had set out.

The family were very happy now. Father had a good wage. They had a new house, and the Pit baths were a great benefit. Gradually, they began to put new furniture into their home. One evening when Father came home from the pit. He had his evening meal, as usual. Then he said to Jason, "Everything in our home is just lovely. I think that you should put my Miner's lamp in your bedroom". Jason, often used to polish up his Father's lamp, so it was shining bright. He felt that he was growing up, and that his Father could trust him to be a good reliable son in the family. So Jason took the Miner's lamp up to his bedroom, and put it beside the bed. That night he smiled to himself, and fell asleep.

Half way through the next morning, in class at school, the Pit Siren gave out its warning blast of an accident at the Pit. All the Rescue Squad were already putting on their breathing apparatus, to go down the pit. The ambulances were standing by. The Fire Brigade was rushing to help. Jason was so worried that he dashed out of the school. He reached the Pit, but already there were many anxious women at the gate before him. The Manager read out a statement to the waiting crowd. There had been an accident. Underneath, there had been a massive fall of stones and rocks, and some miners had been working at the site. They had been hurt.

Jason's Father had been one of the miners who had been hurt. They brought the miners up on stretchers, in the Pit lift. Jason saw men gently lift his Father into an ambulance, and off they went to the hospital. Jason's mother rang the hospital later, and was told that Father had cuts and bruises, and was suffering from shock, but that he would soon recover. Other men had been killed. Jason said a prayer of thanks to God that father was not dead. He remembered that Father had given him the Miner's lamp the evening before. In his bedroom, Jason polished the Miner's lamp once more. He went to visit his Father at the Hospital. He was proud that his Father had been a Miner, who risked his life for other people. "I've polished the lamp", Father, he said. "Get well and come home soon."

Prayer:

> Lord, help us to remind ourselves
> of the good people who work for us.
> Bless all those who have dangerous jobs,
> and bring them safe home again in the evening,
> to their families and friends.
> Bless anyone who has been injured
> through an accident at work.   Amen.

Hymn:

> Give me oil in my lamp. (C&P.l. 43)

Teachers' Note: (1). We ought to be thankful for people who work in dangerous jobs for us. (2). Family life is a loving and very precious thing. (3). Many people do dirty, but important jobs, in coal pits, factories, and in waste disposal.

(b) The Youth Club
Week 10   Sad and Glad Events

The village Youth Club had kept paint in the cellar. They had just been decorating the club. The walls looked fresh and clean. The remaining unused paint might be of use in the future, to brighten any wood-work that needed repainting. So the Youth Leader decided to store it in the cellar. The members of the Youth Club had worked very hard. They themselves had raised the money to redecorate the rooms. One night after everyone had gone home, a number of teenages, who were not Club members, broke the lock on the cellar door. They entered the cellar and found the cans of paint carefully stored away.

These thoughtless young people opened the cans, and used the paint to write slogans on the walls, inside and outside the Youth Club. They left behind paint spilled all over the cellar floor. They thought that no-one would know who had caused the mess. Using the back door, they escaped and made their way home in the darkness.

Next morning, the Youth Leader was very upset to find that someone had broken open the door of the cellar, and had left a mess behind them. He telephoned the Police Station, and told the Sergeant what had happened.

Two policemen came down in their car to the Youth Club. The Youth Leader showed the policemen the damage. The policemen and the Youth Leader decided to appeal to the good nature of the members of the Club. They all met together for a discussion that evening. The Club members knew that their members would not want to damage their own Club.

As the discussion continued, one girl suggested that the members themselves should become Detectives, and try to solve the crime. The boys thought that this was a good idea, since they did not want to give the other Club members a bad name in the village. The girls also agreed to take part in the investigation.

After going down to the cellar, the Youth Club members realised that the guilty people had walked on the paint, and that the paint had been under their shoes. Their footprints marked the floor. Red paint was mixed with cream, blue, brown, and white. The foot prints were clearly seen. They first examined the Club members shoes, to see if they had any paint on their soles. They were relieved to find that no Club member had paint on their shoes.

The Club members went outside, and found paint foot-prints going up the road, and into one of the side avenues. The Club members followed the foot-prints, until they turned into three different garden paths, leading to houses. When they knocked on the doors, the parents were most helpful. The parents investigated their own houses, found paint marks on carpets, and stairs. The individual parents questioned their three lads, and they admitted that they had broken into the Youth Club cellar. The three lads did not realise, that in the darkness, they had left a trail of paint behind them, even in their own homes. On the soles of their shoes was the mixed paint, the evidence indicating that they had been inside the Cellar.

The parents made the offenders apologise to the members of the Youth Club Committee. They admitted their thoughtless deed. The three lads declared that they were truly sorry for all the trouble which they had caused. The Club members decided not to take the matter any further. The offenders were made to pay compensation to the Club for the loss of the paint. The offenders volunteered to help clean up the cellar, and to remove the slogans they had written on the walls.

The young offenders realised that they had brought disgrace upon their parents, and families. The local policemen would keep an eye on their future behaviour. However, the Youth Club members were a kindly crowd of young people. At the next Committee meeting, they agreed to ask the three offenders to become members of the Club. In making this invitation, they meant to forgive and forget what had happened. The three lads accepted the invitation, and became good reliable members. They never gave the Club, nor the police, any trouble again.

Prayer:

> Father God, we thank you for Youth Leaders.
> We thank you for Youth Clubs,
> and the young people who support them.
> We pray that our young people,
> may become reliable in daily life.
> May we have respect for other people,
> and be a good example in our Community.   Amen.

Hymn:

> The building Song. (C&P.l. 61)

Teachers' Note: (1). Youth Clubs are kept open for the use of young people in the Community. (2). Young people often are thoughtless in their foolish behaviour. They may bring disgrace upon the Parents. (3) We ought to recognise that young people who have made mistakes in the past, may have changed their behaviour, and become reliable again.

(c) Joseph's Coat

Week 10   Sad and Glad Tidings

Parents should never love one child more than another. Good parents love all of their children in an equal manner. There was one a father, by the name of Jacob, who had twelve sons. He was a farmer. He loved all twelve of his sons, but he loved Joseph in a special way. Because there were twelve sons, they were of different ages. Benjamin was the youngest, and Reuben was the eldest. Some were grown men, and some were growing boys.

One day Jacob, the father, gave a special present to his favourite son, Joseph. He gave him a coat of many colours. If anyone should have been given the coat, it ought to have been Reuben, since he was the first-born. Giving the coat of many colours to Joseph had one result. It made the other sons of Jacob very jealous of Joseph.

Joseph used to tell his brothers about his dreams. His dreams were usually about the other brothers bowing down to him. This made them even more angry.

One day Jacob sent Joseph to Dothan, to find out whether his brothers and their flocks were safe. When his brothers saw Joseph approaching, they said,"Look the Dreamer is coming, let us kill him".

Reuben the oldest brother persuaded the brothers not to kill Joseph, but to tie him up and throw him into a well. Reuben meant to come back alone later in the evening, to set Joseph free, and to send him back to his father. However, when Reuben was away caring for the sheep, some merchant-traders on camels passed on their way to Egypt. The brothers sold Joseph as a slave to the merchant-traders for twenty pieces of silver. When the merchants arrived in Egypt, they sold Joseph as a slave to Potiphar, who was an officer of Pharaoh, the King of Egypt.

The brothers took Joseph's beautiful coloured coat, and stained it with the blood of a goat. They showed the blood-stained coat to Jacob, and Jacob wept, because he thought that Joseph had been killed by some wild animal.

Joseph was such a good slave that Potiphar put Joseph in charge of his household and his business. Potiphar's wife plotted against Joseph and he was thrown into prison. When King Pharaoh needed someone to interpret his dreams, Joseph was the one man who could do so. He warned Pharaoh that his dream meant that the harvest would fail, and that a famine was approaching Egypt.

Joseph was appointed ruler, second to Pharaoh. He wore the King's ring on his finger, and the King's gold chain around his neck. Joseph stored up the corn during seven years of plenty, and he opened the store-houses and sold corn to the people, during the seven years when the harvest failed. He became famous, rich, and powerful. His brothers did not know that God had protected Joseph, or that he had been made ruler, next to the King. They came to Egypt to buy corn. Joseph made the brothers bring Benjamin next time they came.

They brought Benjamin, and Joseph revealed himself to his brothers. He explained to them, how God had used him, to keep his own family alive, as well as saving Egypt from starvation. He was very happy to learn that his old father, Jacob was still alive. They brought Jacob, now an old man into Egypt. Joseph could not wait, but went out in his chariot to meet his father. They wept tears of joy, and hugged each other. Joseph provided a house for his father and brothers in Egypt.

Prayer:

> Father God, we thank you,
> that Joseph provided corn for bread,
> when the harvests failed in Egypt.
> We pray for all those parts of our world,
> where people are hungry today.
> Help the rulers of the world to share out the food,
> that there may be enough for all.   Amen.

Hymn:

He's got the whole world. (C&P.l. 19)

Teachers' Note: (1) Parents should never have a favourite child. They should love each one equally. (2) Joseph was used by God to save Egypt from starvation, and also to save his own family. (3) When Joseph was powerful, he never took revenge on his brothers. He forgave them. See Genesis Chapters 37-47 for the full story of Joseph.

(a) Disobedient Dougal   *Week 11   Togetherness*

The two girls lived in a large country house. They owned a lovely little white West Highland Terrier. They gave their little dog the name of "Dougal". They loved him very much. He was a beautiful dog, and the dog loved the two girls. They bathed him when he became muddy. The girls loved to brush his white fur. They bought a special basket as a bed for Dougal. He liked to lie in the basket, and go to sleep, Everyone admired Dougal when he was taken outside for a walk. There was only one problem. Dougal was very often a disobedient little dog.

The park-keeper put up a sign next to the pond in Winter which read. "Do not walk on the ice on the pond. It is dangerous!" The two girls called Dougal, when he went near the pond, and proceeded to scold him. The little dog would wag his tail at them, and go off racing ahead of them on the frosty grass. Soon he had raced on the ice on the pond. "Crash", the ice had broken! Dougal had fallen in to the water. The girls had to wade in to knee depth in the cold pond, to pull him out again. He certainly was a disobedient little dog.

At home, he would run upstairs and lie on the beds, just where he knew he ought not to be. Each time he was brought down-stairs again, he would lie beside the fire. When no one was looking, he would quietly slip upstairs and lie on the beds again. One day, when Mother brought sausages home from the butcher, and set them on the kitchen table, Dougal jumped on the chair, and then on to the table. He ate the sausages when no one was looking. Mother became very cross with him. When he was seen to be halfway up the stairs on his way to the bed-room, the girls would call him down again, but he would sit at the top of the stairs, and growl. He was disobedient, and would not come downstairs.

He would often run out into the garden to chase the cats. Sometimes he would go into the garden next door, and try to pull the washing off the line. When the dustmen came to empty the bins, Dougal would bark so furiously, as if he were ten times bigger than he really was. Dougal had no road sense. Sometimes he would crawl under the garden hedge, and sit in the middle of the road, so that lorries and cars would have to screech to a halt.. He was really both disobedient, and a mischievous dog. Yet everyone loved him.

One dark evening, Dougal slipped under the fence, and ran across the road into another garden. A large dog in the other garden chased him back again. As he ran back across the road, he was knocked down by a car and injured. The car did not stop. Everyone was very sad because Dougal had been injured. The girls cried as they cuddled him. However, the Vet called to examine his injuries. He suggested that Dougal should be taken to the animal Clinic and be x-rayed, to see whether any bones were broken. Dougal was kept at the animal Clinic for ten days, until he had fully recovered from his injuries; Then he was allowed home again.

The girls were delighted to have Dougal back again. Everyone agreed that if only Dougal had been an obedient dog, he would not have been knocked down by the car. Dougal never liked being on the road again, but he was very happy in the fields and woodlands. At home he became as happy as he had been before. When he could not be found downstairs, where do you think the girls would find him?

Prayer:

> Father God, help us to value school rules,
> and to obey our parents.
> Help us to obey the Law.
> Teach us to understand the Ten Commandments.
> We thank you for any good advice
> received from other people.   Amen.

Hymn:

> Who put the colours in the rainbow? (C&P.l. 12)

Teachers' Note: (1) Being together requires obedience to some rules. (2) Sometimes we harm ourselves, or someone else, when we are disobedient. (3) Dougal is an example of a lovable little dog who was injured by a car. It does not mean that all children who have been knocked down on the road have been disobedient.

(b) The Team Spirit   *Week 11   Togetherness*

In the year 1859 Blondin, a Frenchman tied a tight-rope across the Niagara Falls. The rushing mighty waters of the river Niagara, flow over the rocks in a great torrent of spray at this point. The Falls are situated between cliffs on the

Canadian side, and the cliffs on the American side. Blondin was a highly skilled tight-rope trapeze artiste. He could walk along a rope or a thin wire very easily. Crowds of people loved to watch him doing his feats. Blondin easily walked across the tightrope, despite the danger of falling into the river below.

Next time Blondin brought with him a small gas stove. He walked across the tight-rope, half way. He then stopped on the rope, and cooked an omelette on a gas camping cooker on the rope. He completed his meal, before he continued his walk across the river on the tight-rope. People were utterly amazed at his skill and balance.

Another time, Blondin wheeled a wheel-barrow on the rope, across the river. Everyone, thought that he was wonderful. One tourist who was watching Blondin, came up to him and said, "I think that you are the best tight-rope artiste in the world". Blondin looked at the tourist, and spoke out before everyone. "Very good, my friend. If you really think that I am the best in the world, are you willing to sit in my wheel-barrow, and I will wheel you across the Niagara Falls?" The man shrank back in fear. "No thank you," he said. Blondin answered the man by saying, "If you really believed that I was the best in the world, then you would not be afraid to get into the wheel-barrow". What Blondin meant was that the man did not really trust him.

Now for a second story about trust. Sam wanted to learn to swim. He was only ten years of age, but he was afraid of the water. When all the children were splashing in and out of the swimming pool, Sam just clung to the side of the pool. He was afraid. The swimming Teacher did not have much success with Sam, because Sam could not relax in the water. Finally, Sam's Dad took him to the swimming pool during the evening. Dad carried Sam out a little way into the pool, and held him up in the water, in order to to teach him to float on his back. Sam was terrified. He became rigid in the water.

Dad could see now why Sam could not learn to swim. Dad said, "Now Sam, I want to teach you to relax in the water. You must trust me. My arms are going to be underneath you all the time, so I want you to relax." Sam trusted his Dad. He began to become relaxed, knowing that Dad's arms were underneath him. As he relaxed in the pool, he felt himself beginning to float a little. In a short time that evening he had learnt to float on his back without fear. He could move his hands and felt himself move a little in the water. As he trusted his Dad beside him in the water, Sam soon learnt to swim.

Later on in life, Sam learnt that he had to learn to trust many people. He played in the football team, so he had to learn to pass the ball, and trust his team to score goals. Sometimes they did not do it very well! Nevertheless, Sam trusted his team to do their best on the field. Later on, Sam grew up, and became interested in climbing mountains. He often was tied by a rope to other members of the climbing party, and he learnt that on dangerous mountains, they all trusted each other.

A team may be as small as two people, or as large as a school. Being together means that we must learn to trust each other.

Prayer:

> Lord, create in us the team spirit.
> Help us in this school to trust each other.
> Let us not be fearful of others,
> or selfish, wanting our own way.
> Rather, let us help each other.
> Bless every Teacher and pupil in our school.   Amen.

Hymn:

> He's got the whole world. C&P.l. 19)

Teachers' Note: (1) The team spirit in a school is a strong force for good. (2). A Team may be as small as two people, or an entire school may work together for the common good. (3) Togetherness is helpful for everyone!

(c) A Lame Beggar   *Week 11   Togetherness*

It happened after Jesus had died on the cross, and after he had arisen from the dead. One day he was standing with his disciples on the Mount of Olives. Jesus told them that he was going to leave them, and go back to his Father in Heaven. Then he seemed to ascend upwards, and he vanished out of their sight. The disciples knew that they no longer had a leader on earth, whom they could see. Their trust now was in God.

The disciples made their homes in Jerusalem for a time. One day, both Peter and John were going up to worship God at the Temple. It was during the third hour of the afternoon, at the hour of prayer. A lame beggar man was lying at the Beautiful gate of the Temple. It was customary to leave blind, lame, or handicapped people at this gate. People going into the Temple to worship God, often gave money to the poor and needy people who sat or lay around the Temple gate.

This particular beggar man asked for money from Peter and John. Peter spoke to the lame Beggar. He said, "Look at us. We have no silver or gold in our pockets to give to you. But what I have I can give. In the name of Jesus of Nazareth, rise up and walk". Peter then took hold of the lame beggar by the right hand. Immediately, the beggar's feet and ankles received strength. A miracle occurred!

The beggar, was no longer lame. He leapt up, and stood, and then walked about. (Lame or handicapped people were not allowed to enter the Temple). The beggar went inside the Temple with Peter and John. He was so happy, that he began to leap, and dance and to praise God for the healing miracle.

The people knew the beggar who used to lie outside the Temple, since he had been there for a long time. They were astonished to see him walking normally again. Peter again spoke. "Do not stare at us, as if we had healed this man by our own power, or holiness. This man has been cured through faith in the name of God's Son, Jesus. This Jesus is the same person whom you killed on a cross. God has raised Jesus from the dead".

The Priests and the Captain of the Temple Guard arrested Peter and John. They put them into prison all night. Later, the authorities allowed Peter and John to go free again, because they had done nothing wrong in making a lame beggar able to walk. After this, Peter and John were able to heal many other sick people in Jerusalem.

In modern times, when we are sick, we are taken to hospital. Doctors and Nurses take care of us until we are well again. Going to hospital and coming out well again, is another kind of miracle. Many hospitals save the lives of many people. Hundreds of years ago, it was the churches who introduced hospitals into our country.

Prayer:

> Father God, we thank you for the healing miracles,
> of Jesus, when he was here on earth.
> We thank you that Peter and John
> were used by God to heal the beggar man.
> We thank you for Doctors and Nurses,
> for Ambulance Workers, and hospitals.   Amen.

Hymn:

> Sad, puzzled eyes. (C&P.2. 74)

Teachers' Note: (1). The lame beggar man had been ill for a long time. (2). Peter said that it was faith in the name of Jesus which had healed the beggar. (3). The Church has always been associated with healing, and hospitals. Doctors and Nurses are Gods servants, when they help to heal their patients.

(a) Aiming and Growing

All good things come to an end! The school year is another period of life that has an ending. Children will know that the "Calendar Year" begins in January, and that it ends in December. The "School Year" begins after the Summer holidays, and it ends just before the next Summer holidays. There are two ways of looking at the end of the School Year.

1.   THE END OF THE SCHOOL YEAR IS LIKE AIMING AT A TARGET.

The people of Switzerland love the story of William Tell. When Switzerland was ruled by Austria, there was a local ruler by the name of Gessler, whom everyone hated. Gessler was a cruel ruler. He once ordered that a cap, with the badge of the King of Austria on it, should be hung on a a pole in the village square. He commanded that everyone who passed by the cap should bow to it. Unfortunately that day, William Tell was up in the mountains. He did not know about Gessler's order.

The next day, William Tell was walking through the village square, with his son, and he happened to pass the the cap on the pole. He did not bow to it. Gessler saw him, and William Tell and his son were arrested. Everyone knew that William Tell was an expert shot with the cross-bow. Being a cruel man, Gessler ordered that William Tell's son should be tied to a stake, with an apple placed on the top of the boy's head.

Then Gessler ordered William Tell to shoot the apple from his son's head with an arrow from his cross-bow. If he could split the apple, then both William Tell and his son would be set free. If he failed, both of them would be killed. William Tell begged the cruel Gessler to change his mind, because no father would risk killing his own son. However, the boy believed so much in his father's skill with the cross-bow, that he shouted to his father, "I'll keep perfectly still, Father. You have practised for years; you can do it."

William Tell took two arrows, and put one arrow in his long leather boot. The other he put into his cross-bow. He took very careful aim, and the arrow flew to its target, splitting the apple in two pieces. Then William Tell said to Gessler, "You will notice that I took two arrows. Had I missed the apple and killed my son, the second arrow would have pierced your heart." Off went William Tell and his son, back to his home on the mountain. Gessler shook with fear at how near he came to being killed at that moment.

The end of school term is like a target, at which we all aim. We all try to do our very best right to the very end of the year. We aim to be better at reading. Our hand-writing should have improved. If you are practising swimming, or foot-ball, or P.E., then you will have been aiming at a target improvement for yourself.

The older pupils have been aiming at the day when they will leave the Junior School, and know enough, to take their place at the High school Like an arrow, you all have reached your target. Some may have scored high marks, by reaching a "Bull's Eye". Others maybe will do better next year.

Most of you look forward to going into a higher class next year. This means you have a more difficult target next School Year.

2. THE END OF THE SCHOOL YEAR IS ABOUT GROWING UP.

Paula received a little furry puppy for her birthday. Her Dad had said that it was a little St. Bernard pup. He said that St. Bernard dogs were used in Switzerland to find, and rescue people, who were lost in snow avalanches on the mountains. These dogs had such a strong sense of smell that the could scent-out people lying trapped under the snow. Dad also said that they sometimes carried a little barrel of brandy tied around their neck, for people suffering from the cold. The brandy acted like medicine and warmed up the survivors enough, to allow them to be taken down the mountain alive.

Paula loved her little puppy, and she named him "Benny". Paula made him a bed out of a cardboard box. In three months time, the pup had grown bigger, so she used a large apple box instead. The pup did not stop growing. In another three months, Paula had to use a tea chest for his bed. At the end of the first year, even the tea chest was too small. Her father had to ask a Carpenter to make Benny a special warm wooden kennel, outside the house. He had grown just too big, to stay inside. St. Bernard dogs are really out-door dogs. Of course, she would sometimes have Benny inside , and he would lie down, sprawled over the rug, leaving no room for anyone else's feet. He was just too big to keep in the living room. Paula would look at the photographs she had taken of her little puppy, when she first had him. She could not believe that any dog could have grown so quickly.

Children are just like Benny, they too grow up quickly. They begin school in the infants class. They move up through the classes, growing all the time, until they reach the top class. Then they have to move up to the High school. Children should take a look at their old shoes, or their old clothes. They will now find that such items are many sizes too small for them to wear. They have grown out of them, and they no longer fit.

Best of all, children grow in understanding. They have to begin to learn to read in the Infant Reception class. Each year they learn more about their environment and about themselves.

Leaving school from the top class is a happy adventure. Older pupils will love the High school with its new freedom and responsibilities. They will be in the first class of a High school! The end of the School year is also a little sad, because older pupils will be leaving behind their Teachers, and their Junior school friends.

Perhaps,they will soon be wearing a new school uniform. Everyone in the school will be growing up and moving up a class. The end of the School Year is both a happy and a sad occasion. Here is a prayer for everyone at this time.

Prayer:

> Father God, we thank you for this school.
> We thank you for all our Teachers,
> and for all that we have learnt this year.
> Help us to aim high, and to grow up,
> to be happy and intelligent pupils.
> Bless everyone in the top class
> who are leaving for the High School this year.   Amen.

Hymn:

> You shall go out with joy. (C&P.2. 98)

Teacher's Note: (1) We all need to aim at targets and to better ourselves. (2) Whether we like it or not, we cannot stop growing up, and growing older. It is good to accept this onward movement as a happy adventure in life. (3) We ought never to forget the kindness of our teachers and friends over the past years. God bless you!

(b) A Trip to Paris

Week 12   End of School Year

There is another kind of learning, which is seeing exciting things for oneself, instead of reading about them in books. Twelve of the children, from the top class, in the school, who were leaving for the High School at the end of the School Year (six boys and six girls), went on a trip to Paris. Three Teachers went with them.

They travelled by train to Dover harbour. Then, they sailed in a large ferry boat, which carried cars, coaches, and lorries in the decks below. While passengers enjoyed the upper decks. The children and their Teachers were free to walk around the ferry. They enjoyed spending money in the duty free shop, and had their lunch in the ship's cafeteria. When they arrived at Calais, they transferred to the new fast train which travelled to Paris at high speed.

The children were enjoying everything they saw and heard. Their Teachers explained that not being able to enjoy a conversation with people, was a good reason for their learning the French language as soon as possible. They noticed that in the hotel bedroom, in a chest of drawers was a Bible in three languages; French, English and German.

Next day they went to see the famous Arc de Triomphe. (A Triumphal Arch.) This was a large stone arch, built on the orders of Napoleon, and begun in 1806. The arch commemorates the victories of the French armies, and of the Revolution. There are many names, and pictures cut into the stone. In 1920, this great arch became the site of the Tomb of the unknown French soldier.

The Teachers took them to see the Cathedral of Notre Dame, (Our Lady). The Cathedral had been built on an Island on the river Seine, which flows through Paris. Later they were delighted to see the Cathedral flood-lit.

They visited the Louvre, the most famous Picture Gallery in the world. Hundreds of Paintings were hanging on the walls of the many rooms of the great building. They saw the famous painting, "Mona Lisa", by the artist, Leonardo de Vinci. They viewed the Glass Pyramid entrance building. It looked like a large glass-house sitting in front of the Palace building. Everyone agreed that it was an exciting building to see.

"Let us go to see the Eiffel Tower now," the children said. So off they went. They gazed at the tall iron structure built high into the sky. It had been erected for the World Fair of 1889. The Teacher explained that the great metal Tower was designed so that the pressure at ground level was only that of someone sitting on a chair. Painters were continually working on it.

Time was passing. They had a meal in one of the French out-door cafes. Since the weather was warm, they sat at tables in the street, under a striped canvas canopy. The children ordered "Crepes", which were like large delicious pancakes rolled up, with syrup inside them. They said, "Merci" (Thank You!) to the Waiter.

The party went to see a building near the entrance to Montparnasse Railway station. They could not believe that they were going up to the fifty-sixth floor. A lift took them there in moments.

They walked around the top floor, looking out of the windows on all sides of the building. They had splendid views of the City of Paris. People and cars looked like little toys down below. They went up yet another flight of inside steps, and they came out into an viewing area, like a school play-ground with high railings around it. It was a beautiful sunny day, and the children soon lost their fear of heights. They knew that they were safe. All around they could see the wonderful sights of Paris.

The Teachers smiled, and one said to the children, "We have not held a Worship assembly for several days. Let us do it now while no-one is about." The children bowed their heads, and said the Lord's Prayer together." They were all strangely moved. Making their way downwards again, the children realised that they had a wonderful experience, which they never would forget! When they all arrived back home in England, they had so much to tell their Parents and friends.

Prayer:

> Lord, we thank you for holidays.
> We thank you for the end of the School Year.
> As we look back, we remember how much we have grown,
> and how much more we understand, than last year.
> Teach us to continue to observe our world,
> and to learn by seeing, and hearing.
> Through Jesus Christ our Lord.   Amen.

Hymn:

> The journey of life. (C&P.l. 45)

Teachers' Note: (1) There are other ways to learn, apart from reading books. We may learn from watching Nature, or other People. (2) The end of the School Year could be the beginning of exciting new knowledge. (3) If you are away from home, you may know that God is always near you.

(c) End of Term Reports   *Week 12   End of School Year*

At the end of the School Year, each Pupil is given a School Report to take home to their Parents. Most reports are honest accounts of the Pupil's progress during the year. Parents like to read their children's report.

Jesus had four reports written by four different people about his life's work. There are four Gospels, known to us as St. Matthew, St. Mark, St. Luke, and St. John. These Gospel books tell us about the parables, and the miracles of healing performed by Jesus. They tell us about his birth in a Stable. They tell us about him as a boy in the Temple. They tell us about his death on the cross. Most important of all, they tell us about his resurrection from the dead on the first Easter morning.

When we go to the Doctor's, or into hospital, someone writes down a progress report on our health. We make and keep reports because it is helpful in the future, to know what has happened to us in the past. Some people keep diaries, which are really reports made by ourselves.

Jamie Simpson was very poor indeed. When he had holes in his socks, his mother used to darn the socks with old wool. They did not have enough money to buy new ones. Jamie was a very bright little boy at school, and worked so hard at his lessons, that he had good reports at the end of every year. In those days, only people who could pay could stay on at school, and go to college. Jamies's brothers worked hard in the bakery, to earn enough money to send Jamie to

College. Jamie became a famous Doctor, and was later known as Sir. James Simpson.

Jamie Simpson became famous because he invented Chloroform. When people needed an operation, Doctors often had to cut open their patients bodies, which caused so much pain, that often the patients died of shock. The pain endured by the patients was terrible.

Dr. Jamie Simpson studied very long hours searching for an anaesthetic, which could be used to give patients a painless operation. Finally, he invented a gas named Chloroform, which enabled Doctors to put the patient to sleep, before an operation. The Doctors now could cut the patient's body open, repair the inside of the body, and sew the body up again, while the patient slept through the operation, feeling absolutely nothing at all. Patients experienced no shock after the operation, and so thousands of lives were saved. Many children have had their tonsils removed, under Chloroform. All because of the work of the little boy, Jamie Simpson, who had the good School Year Reports.

Sometimes a Pupil's intelligence develops later than others in the school. A very ordinary boy or girl may develop into a very clever scholar as they grow older. In a little school at the seaside town, Portrush, in Northern Ireland, there was a pupil by the name of Adam Clarke. His Headteacher used very cruel words about him, when Adam was twelve years old. He declared that Adam Clarke was the most stupid boy in the school. However, Adam, was a late developer. He became a distinguished linguist, and scholar. He studied many languages. He knew Hebrew, Latin, Greek and Aramaic, and eventually he wrote a famous Commentary on the all the books of the Bible.

He became a famous Methodist Minister, and if you ever go to visit Portrush, you will find a church there, named after him. If you look carefully, outside the church you will also read an inscription to his honour. So his School Report would have been wrong, he was not the most stupid boy after all, but one of the most intelligent Pupils which the school had ever produced. Dr. Adam Clarke later in life became very interested in the people of the Shetland Islands off the coast of Scotland. The people loved him as a Minister, because he showed them such love and care.

School Reports are a good guide to our present progress. They do not tell us who will be future Prime Ministers, or famous Athletes on the sportsfield. Maybe some ordinary boy or girl from our own school, will later surprise everyone, by becoming a world famous personality! It is more likely that most of our Pupils will make good and honest work people, whatever their skills. They will be the Parents of the future generation.

Prayer:

Father God, we are at the end of the school year.
We have tried to do our very best at lessons.
As we receive our Reports, may we not be discouraged.
Help us to do better next year.
We thank you again for our school,
and our Teachers and other Staff.   Amen.

Hymn:

He made me. (C&P.l. 18)

Teachers' Note: (1) School Reports are a record of Pupils' individual progress in class. Children should not be discouraged by them, if they are genuinely trying to give of their best. It is always possible to improve with time. (2) School Reports have a reference to the Pupils' personalities and present abilities and skills. More than this, they should have gained from the "unseen curriculum", which is the ethos of a particular class-room, or school. (3) Children have in them, the ability of surprising the world of their worth!